Jokes, Puns, and Riddles

David Allen Clark

JOKES, PUNS, AND RIDDLES

Illustrated by Lionel Kalish

DOUBLEDAY & COMPANY, INC., GARDEN CITY, NEW YORK

For Kathy,

Who made it happen

Contents

8 CONTENTS

Jokes, Puns, and Riddles

BRAIN TEASERS

Ron: Did you know that a grasshopper can jump a distance that is fifty times its own length?

Don: No, but I've seen a wasp lift a 250-pound man three feet off the ground.

Frank: If one man has two sacks of grain and another
    has three sacks, which man has the heavier load?
Hank: The man with three sacks.
Frank: No, the man with three has nothing but sacks.

Ned: Do you know why the electric bill is figured in
    kilowatts?
Red: Because you pay for all those watts that were
    killed as they went through the meter.

A duck, a frog, and a skunk went to the movies.
Tickets were a dollar each. Who got in, and who
didn't? The duck got in because he had a bill. The
frog got in on his green back. But the poor skunk
couldn't get in because he had only a (s)cent, and it
was a bad one.

Why are fire engines red?
    Two and two are four; four times three is twelve;
twelve inches make a ruler; a famous ruler was Queen
Elizabeth; the *Queen Elizabeth* sails the ocean; the
ocean is full of fish; fish have fins; the Finns fought
the Russians; Russians are red—so fire engines are red
because they are always rushin'.

Larry: If there were a bank holdup, who would be the
    main witness?
Barry: Who?
Larry: The teller.

Mack: Did you hear about the race between the head of cabbage, the faucet, and the tomato?

Jack: No, how did it end up?

Mack: The cabbage was ahead, the faucet was running, and the tomato was trying to ketchup.

Math Teacher: Johnny, if you mowed the lawn for twenty-five people and they each paid you a dollar and a quarter, what would you get?

Johnny: A new bicycle.

Tim: I know of something that occurs once in every minute, twice in every moment, but not once in a hundred thousand years.

Jim: What is it?

Tim: The letter *M*.

Polly: What's bigger when it's upside down?

Olly: I don't know. What?

Polly: The number 6.

Ann: What lives in the winter, dies in the summer, and grows with its roots upward?

Dan: What?

Ann: An icicle.

Nick: Is it legal in this state for a man to marry his widow's sister?

Rick: Of course not. That man would be dead.

Ron: John, do you think if a man smashed a clock, he could be accused of killing time?

John: Not if the clock struck first.

Question: How many wives is a man given by the minister in the marriage service?

Answer: Sixteen—four better, four worse, four richer, four poorer.

Ike: How do you make notes of stone?
Mike: I don't know.
Ike: Just rearrange the letters.

Smarty: What runs around town all day and lies down
all night with its tongue hanging out?
Arty: I have no idea.
Smarty: Your shoe, silly!

Ed: Why are laws like the ocean?
Ted: I have no idea.
Ed: Because the most trouble is caused by the breakers.

Al: Two men were playing checkers. They played five
games, and each man won the same number of
games.
Pal: That's impossible.
Al: No, it isn't. They were playing different people.

Sam: When the clock strikes thirteen, what time is it?
Pam: There is no such time.
Sam: Yes there is. It's time to get it fixed.

Smarty: Some months have thirty days, some thirty-one,
but how many months have twenty-eight days?
Arty: February.
Smarty: Nope—all of them do.

Ted: If the green house is on the left side of the road, and the red house is on the right side of the road, where is the white house?

Fred: How am I supposed to know?

Ted: Easy. It's in Washington.

Paul: If you had only one match and entered a room in which there was a kerosene lamp, an oil heater, and a wood-burning stove, which would you light first?

Saul: The stove?

Paul: No, you'd have to light the match first.

Don: There was a girl in the candy store who was five feet tall and wore size eight shoes. What did she weigh?

Ron: I have no idea.

Don: It's easy. Candy.

Stu: I have in my hand two U.S. coins which total fifty-five cents. One is not a nickel. What are the two coins?

Sue: I don't know.

Stu: One is a fifty-cent-piece—the *other* is a nickel.

Matt: How many sides has a circle?

Pat: None.

Matt: You're wrong. There are two—inside and out-side.

Jeff: There were three men in a boat with four cigarettes but no matches. What did they do?

Eff: I give up. What?

Jeff: They threw out one cigarette and made the boat a cigarette lighter.

DAFFINITIONS

Impassable—A wet football.

The Beatles—A barbershop quartet that did not get waited on.

Astronomer—A night watchman.

World—A jigsaw puzzle with a peace missing.

Depth—Height turned upside down.

Ginger Ale—A drink that feels like your foot when it goes to sleep.

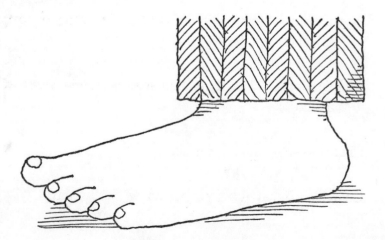

Generally—The head of the Confederate Army.

An Archeologist—A man whose career lies in ruins.

Bacteria—The rear entrance to a cafeteria.

Beatle School—A place to learn reeling, writhing, and a rhythmic tick.

Raisin—A worried grape. ✓

Skeleton—A guy inside out with his outside off.

Research—When you look for something twice.

Expert—*X* is a mathematical term meaning unknown, and a spurt is a drip under pressure—so an expert is an unknown drip under pressure.

Psychiatrist—A man who doesn't have to worry as long as other people do.

Atomic Bomb—The thing that makes molehills out of mountains.

Cheerios—Hula-hoops for ants. ✓

Coincide—What most people do when it rains.

Synonym—A word you use when you can't spell the other one.

√Iceberg—A kind of permanent wave.

Professor—A textbook wired for sound.

Nonsense—An elephant hanging over a cliff with his tail tied to a daisy.

Volcano—A mountain that blew its stack.

Television—A machine that offers people who don't have anything to do a chance to watch people who can't do anything.

Wholesome—The only thing from which you can take the whole and still have some left.

A Caterpillar—An upholstered worm.

Mountain Climber—A man who always wants to take just one more peak.

Politics—A parrot that has swallowed a watch.

√X-Ray—Bellyvision.

√ Pillow—Headquarters.

Soda Jerk—A licensed fizzician.

Undercover Agent—A spy in bed.

Mountain Range—A cooking stove made specially for use at high altitudes.

Etiquette—Saying "No, thank you," when you want to yell, "Gimme."

Circle—A round line with no kinks in it, joined up so as not to show where it began.

Icicle—An eavesdropper.

Sick Reptile—An illigator.

Alarm Clock—Something to scare the daylight into you.

Tricycle—A tot rod.

Tomorrow—One of the greatest labor-saving devices of today.

Hatchet—What a hen does to an egg.

Cactus—An overgrown pin cushion.

Mosquito—A flying hypodermic needle.

Conference—A meeting of the bored.

Suit of Armor—A knightgown.

Pipecleaner—A toothpick with long underwear.

Wedding Ring—A tourniquet worn on the left hand to
     stop circulation.

Pasteurize—Too far to see.

Rubber Gloves—Things you can put on and then wash
     your hands without getting them wet.

Advertising—The art of making you think you've
     longed all your life for something you never heard
     of before.

Actor—Someone who tries to be everything but himself.

Criminal—One who gets caught.

Cabbage—The age of a taxi.

Pyramid—An organized pile of rocks.

Long-haired Music—A Monkee's album.

Cannibal—A person who is fed up with people.

SHARPS AND FLATS

Len: Yesterday I lit a cigarette with a twenty-dollar bill.
Glen: That was pretty extravagant, wasn't it?
Len: Not really. It was a bill from my grocer, and I
    didn't intend to pay it anyway.

Ron: How did you like the play last night?

Don: I saw the first act, but not the second.

Ron: Why didn't you stay?

Don: I couldn't wait that long. It said on the program "Two Years Later."

Mandy: If I see a field full of cows, how can I count them quickly?

Candy: I don't know, how?

Mandy: Count their hoofs and divide by four.

Bill: How was spaghetti invented?

Phil: I have no idea.

Bill: Some fellow used his noodle.

Arty: Ouch! That water burned my hand.

Smarty: You should have felt it before you put your hand in.

Mrs. Fiddledee: What grade eggs do you have?

Grocer: First grade, second grade, and third grade.

Mrs. Fiddledee: Well, I want some that have graduated.

Mr: The laundry must have made a mistake and sent me the wrong shirt. The collar is so tight I can hardly breathe.

Mrs: That's your shirt all right, but you've got your head through the buttonhole.

A painter walked over to a ladder on which his assistant was standing and painting the ceiling.

"Say, Fred," he said, "are you holding on tight to that brush?"

"I sure am," replied Fred. "Why do you ask?"

"Well, in that case," said the painter, "I'd like to borrow the ladder for a few minutes."

A minister wanted to call a minister friend in another city. Picking up the telephone, he said to the operator, "I would like to place a long-distance call."

"Station-to-station?" asked the operator.

"No," said the minister, "parson-to-parson."

Anybody can capture a crocodile. This is how to go about it. First get a telescope, a matchbox, a pair of tweezers, and a large, very boring book. Then choose a steamy hot day and go to the riverbank where crocodiles live. Just sit down, with the telescope, matchbox, and tweezers next to you and start to read. Since the day is warm and the book is dull, you will soon fall asleep.

A crocodile will see you after a while and naturally will come to investigate. He will peer over your shoulder at the book and start to read it. Because the day is hot and the book is dull, he too will fall asleep.

As soon as he does, you wake up. Take the telescope and look at the crocodile through the wrong end. Then, using the tweezers, pick him up and put him into the matchbox. And there you have your crocodile.

Arty: What kind of paper should I use when I make my kite?

Smarty: I'd suggest flypaper.

Ronnie: I'm going to buy a farm two miles long and one-half inch wide.

Connie: What would you raise on a farm that size?

Ronnie: Spaghetti!

Third Grader: Miss Peabody, I've really liked being in your class, and I'm sorry you're not smart enough to teach us next year.

Teacher: You missed school yesterday, didn't you?
Judy: Not a bit.

Fred: Have you ever studied a blotter?
Ned: No, why?
Fred: You should. It's very absorbing.

Pam: What gadget do we use to see through a wall?
Sam: What?
Pam: A window.

Smarty: There were six men standing under one umbrella. Why didn't any of them get wet?
Arty: Why?
Smarty: It wasn't raining.

Ned: This match won't light.
Fred: What's the matter with it?
Ned: I don't know. It worked all right a minute ago.

Harry: Your umbrella looks as though it's seen better days.
Barry: It has had its ups and downs.

Mick: Do you know why Robin Hood robbed only the rich?
Dick: No, why?
Mick: Because the poor didn't have anything.

The advertising agency was making a television commercial about a well-known detergent. The announcer said: "Now, Mrs. Clancy, isn't this the best job of whitening you've ever seen?

"I should say not, young man," said Mrs. Clancy. "But these were my husband's best blue shirts."

Jack: Did you hear about the mad inventor who created a new type of soap?
Mack: No, what kind?
Jack: It's six feet long and eight feet wide. Instead of lifting it to wash yourself, you sit on it and slide up and down.

Meg (answering the phone): Hello.
Voice: Hello, is Boo there?
Meg: Boo who?
Voice: Don't cry little girl. I must have the wrong number.

Polly: Where was simple Simon when the lights were off?
Molly: I have no idea.
Polly: Silly, he was in the dark.

Sam: Why does the Weather Bureau name hurricanes after girls?
Sid: Why?
Sam: If they named them after boys, they would be called himicanes.

Ted: A steam roller ran over my uncle.

Ned: What did you do?

Ted: I just took him home and slipped him under the door.

Sadie: How can you put yourself through a keyhole?

Madie: Tell me. How?

Sadie: Write "yourself" on a piece of paper and push it through a keyhole.

Little Liz: I would like a quarter's worth of bird seed, please.

Saleslady: How many birds do you have, dear?

Little Liz: None, but I want to grow some.

Lady Customer: Can this fur coat be worn in wet weather?

Clerk: Lady, did you ever see a mink carry an umbrella?

Judy: What should you do if you split your sides laughing?

Trudi: I have no idea. What?

Judy: Run until you get a stitch in them.

Mr. Kranz: Well, how are you getting on in your new ten-room house?

Mr. Franz: Oh, not too badly. We furnished the living room by collecting soap coupons.

Mr. Kranz: Didn't you furnish the other nine rooms?

Mr. Franz: We can't yet. They're full of soap.

Ann: I didn't sleep well last night.

Dan: Why not?

Ann: Well, I plugged the electric blanket into the toaster by mistake, and I kept popping out of bed all night.

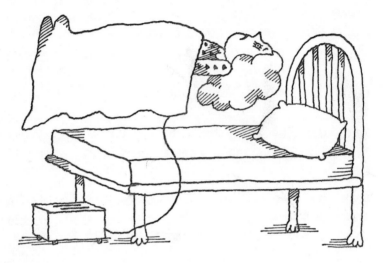

One day a worried-looking man knocked at Mrs. White's door. "I'm terribly sorry, ma'am," he said. "I've just run over your cat, and I'd like to replace it."

"Well," said Mrs. White doubtfully, "it's all right with me. But do you think you can catch mice?"

Meg: When is a shaggy dog most likely to enter a house?

Peg: I don't know, when?

Meg: When the door is open.

The Englishman sat calmly in his garden and watched a flying saucer land. The creature that emerged had three eyes—one orange, one yellow, one green—and fangs. It walked on its elbows, and its nose lit up like a light bulb. "Take me to your leader!" it commanded. "Nonsense," said the Englishman, stirring his tea, "what you need is a plastic surgeon."

Quiz: If you were dying and you only had a nickel, what would you buy?
Whiz: A pack of Life Savers.

Bob: Did you know that there are sixty million TV sets in our country and only forty-five million bath-tubs?
Rob: No, I didn't, but what does that prove?
Bob: Just that there are fifteen million dirty people watching TV.

Eve: I found a snake today but I wasn't afraid of it because it was only a baby.
Steve: How did you know it was only a baby?
Eve: Because it had a rattle.

Two detectives were standing over a dead man named Juan.
First detective: He was killed with a golf gun.
Second detective: What's a golf gun?
First detective: I don't know, but it sure made a hole in Juan.

Curious: Do insects have brains?

Know-It-All: Of course insects have brains. How else could they figure out when you're going to have a picnic?

Jim: How do you avoid falling hair?

Tim: I don't know. How?

Jim: Jump out of the way.

Benny: What have you been doing with yourself lately?
Penny: I've been working on a ranch where they raise hornless goats.
Benny: But . . .
Penny: There are no butts.

Smarty: Want to see something swell?
Arty: Sure!
Smarty: Okay. I'll just hit you on the head with this baseball bat.

There were once three squaws. One sat on a leopard skin. One sat on a doe skin. The third sat on a hippopotamus skin. The squaw on the leopard skin had one son. The squaw on the deer skin had one son. But the squaw on the hippopotamus skin had twin sons. This all goes to prove that the squaw on the hippopotamus is equal to the sons of the squaws on the other two hides.

Question: What flower grows between your nose and your chin?
Answer: Tulips!

Randy: What inventions have helped men get up in the world?
Candy: I give up. Which ones?
Randy: The elevator, the escalator, and the alarm clock.

Sam: How can you get into a locked cemetery at night?
Pam: How?
Sam: Use a skeleton key.

Scoutmaster: Let's get our bearings. You're facing
     north; west is on your left, and east is on your
     right. What's at your back?
Scout: My knapsack!

Arty: Whatever did you do when the ship sank in mid-
     ocean?
Smarty: Oh, I just grabbed a cake of soap and washed
     myself ashore.

Dizzy: Do you know why a hen sitting on a fence is like
     a penny?
Lizzy: No, why?
Dizzy: Because she has a head on one side and a tail
     on the other.

Milly: Can you give an example of period furniture?
Billy: Well, I'd guess an electric chair, because it ends
     a sentence.

Harry: Barry, I heard your nephew drowned in a
     barrel of varnish. It must have been an awful way
     to go.
Barry: No, he had a beautiful finish.

Jenny: What has three eyes and three noses?
Penny: I give up, what?
Jenny: A class vote that is tied.

Dick: Do you mean to tell me you fell over fifty feet
and didn't get a scratch?
Rick: Sure! I was just trying to get to the back of the
bus.

Phil: Aren't you rather warm doing your painting all
bundled up like that?
Bill: Well, it says right here on the paint can to be sure
to put on three coats.

Sadie: Who is Richard Stands?
Madie: I don't know. Who?
Sadie: I don't know either, but he must be pretty
important, because each morning in school we say,
"I pledge allegiance to the Republic of Richard
Stands.

Hank: Why did Tom flood the gym?
Frank: Because the coach asked him to come in as a
sub.

Janie (showing a bathroom scale to a small playmate):
All I know is, you stand on it, and it makes you
mad.

Tim: Did you hear about the boy with the gleam in his eye?

Slim: No, what about him?

Tim: Someone bumped him while he was brushing his teeth.

Cindy: Did you know how many sheep it takes to make one sweater?

Mindy: No. I didn't even know they could knit.

Ronald: Don't you think your new overcoat is rather loud?

Donald: It's all right when I put on a muffler.

Ted: I think our school must be haunted.

Jed: Where did you ever get that idea?

Ted: Well, I always hear people talking about the school spirit.

Two boys were walking past a sign in front of a school, and one said to the other: "Do you know what P.T.A. means?" The other said: "I'm not sure, but I think it means Poor Tired Adults."

Russ: You think you can spell the longest word in the English language? Well let me hear you.

Gus: *S-M-I-L-E-S!*

Russ: That word has only six letters.

Gus: Sure, but there's a mile between the first and last letters.

Linda: I'm disgusted!

Minda: Why?

Linda: I stepped on the scale today, and it said, "One person at a time, please."

Teacher (answering the phone): You say Ben Bones has a bad cold and can't come to school? To whom am I speaking?

Voice (with assumed hoarseness): This is my father.

Great Uncle Harry: How do you like going to school, Albert?

Albert: I like going all right, and I like coming home, too. But I can't stand staying there between times.

Father: What are you scratching your head for, Ferdinand?

Ferdinand: I guess I've got arithmetic bugs.

Father: What are arithmetic bugs?

Ferdinand: Fleas.

Father: Why do you call them arithmetic bugs?

Ferdinand: Because they add to my misery, subtract from my pleasure, divide my attention, and multiply like the dickens.

Connie's mother had invited Mr. and Mrs. Short to dinner. They arrived early. Connie's father was changing his shirt, and her mother was in the kitchen, so Connie went into the living room to entertain the guests.

Mrs. Short said to her husband, "She isn't very *p-r-e-t-t-y*, is she?"

"Maybe not," answered Connie, "but she's very *b-r-i-g-h-t*."

Jimmy's class was having an English lesson, and the teacher called on Jimmy to recite a sentence with a direct object.

After thinking it over, Jimmy stood up and said, "Teacher, everybody thinks you are beautiful."

"Why, thank you, Jimmy," replied the teacher, "but what is the direct object?"

"A good report card next month," was his reply.

Bill: How did you get that black eye?

Will: I got hit by a guided muscle.

Simple: Gee, my hair's full of electricity.
Simon: It sure is! It's connected to a dry cell!

Paul (to his teacher): Miss Bird, I et seven eggs for
    breakfast this morning.
Miss Bird: Ate, Paul.
Paul: I only et seven.
Miss Bird: Ate.
Paul: Well, come to think about it, maybe it was eight
    eggs I et.

Mother: How did you do in your English grammar examination, dear?

Karen: Fine, Mom! I made only one mistake, and I seen it as soon as I done it.

Ned: My little brother is only three, and he can spell his name backwards already!

Fred: That's amazing. What's his name?

Ned: Otto.

Ron and Don were hiking through the woods. Suddenly Ron stopped and sighed deeply. "What's wrong?" asked Don. "Nothing," replied Ron. "But I do wish we had Amy Vanderbilt with us." Don was puzzled. "Why?" he asked. "Because I think we took the wrong fork."

Sandy: Who makes up mystery and horror stories?

Andy: Ghost writers.

Dick: How is a boy scout like a can of apples?

Rick: They are both prepared.

Olly: What did one IBM card say to the other?

Molly: I don't know, what?

Olly: I'm holier than thou.

Teacher (to a boy trying out for a part in the school play): "Have you had any stage experience?"

Boy: "Well, I had my leg in a cast once."

Question: Why did the little boy always stand on a
ladder when he sang his song?
Answer: So he could reach the high notes.

Jim: What is the hardest thing in learning to ride a
bike?
Slim: The pavement.

Police Officer: May I help you, sir?
Elderly Man: I lost a caramel.
Police Officer: Oh, I thought it was important.
Elderly Man: It is. My teeth are in it.

DOWN ON THE FARM

City Slicker: Say, these mosquitoes you have around here are pretty pesky. Don't you ever shoo them?
Farmer: Nope. Too expensive. We just let 'em go barefoot.

City Slicker: Mr. Farmer, why are you plowing your field with a steam roller?
Farmer: I'm raising mashed potatoes this year.

Farmer: I found out how to do the twist last night.

City Slicker: How?

Farmer: All you do is tie oats around your waist and hay around your neck and kinda rotate the crops.

Question: Why is it dangerous to tell a secret on a farm?

Answer: Because the potatoes have eyes, the corn has ears, and the beans talk.

Young Agricultural Student: Your methods of cultivation are terribly out of date. I'd be surprised if you could get ten pounds of apples from that tree.

Old Farmer: So would I. It's a peach tree.

One Sunday a cowboy went to church. When he entered, he saw that he and the preacher were the only ones present. The preacher asked the cowboy if he wanted him to go ahead and preach. The cowboy said, "I'm not too smart, but if I went to feed my cattle and only one showed up, I'd feed him." So the minister began his sermon.

One hour passed, then two hours, then two-and-a-half hours. The preacher finally finished and came down to ask the cowboy how he had liked the sermon. The cowboy answered slowly, "Well, I'm not very smart, but if I went to feed my cattle and only one showed up, I sure wouldn't feed him all the hay."

Farmer Felix had come to the city for the first time and he decided to take a ride on the subway. While waiting for the train, he noticed some candy and chewing-gum machines. He put a penny in one, and when the gum came out, he took the wrapper off and dropped it on the platform. A policeman touched his arm and pointed to a sign that said: DEPOSIT LITTER IN BASKET.

Felix smiled pleasantly. Then he went over to another machine and bought another stick of gum. Again he dropped the wrapper on the platform. This time the policeman said angrily, "Can't you see that sign says DEPOSIT LITTER IN BASKET?"

"Sure," said Felix. "I also see a sign that says DRINK ELBERON BEER and another that says SMOKE LOWNAR KINGS, but I'm minding my own business."

Hillbilly: What'll my boy learn in this here school?
Teacher: History, spelling, trigonometry . . .
Hillbilly: That's fine! Give him lots of that trigonometry; he's the worst shot in the family.

City Slicker: Look at that bunch of cows.
Cowboy: Not *bunch*—herd.
City Slicker: Heard what?
Cowboy: Herd of cows.
City Slicker: Sure I've heard of cows.
Cowboy: No—a cow herd.
City Slicker: Why should I care what a cow heard? I've got no secrets from a cow.

Sid from the city was visiting a farm for the first time and was taken out to see the lambs. He finally mustered enough courage to pet one. "Why, they're made out of blankets!" he exclaimed excitedly.

On one of his rare trips to the city, a hillbilly was so fascinated by a skyscraper's elevators that he stood in front of one for a long time. An old lady, bent and shriveled, entered, a light flashed, and in an instant she was gone. Moments later the same door opened, and out stepped an attractive young woman. Walking away sadly, the hillbilly muttered, "I shoulda brung my old Bessie."

Country Boy: I don't understand why cream is more expensive than milk.

City Slicker: Maybe it's because it's harder for the cows to sit on the small bottles.

City Slicker: What does your son do?

Country Cousin: He's a bootblack in the city.

City Slicker: Oh, I see. You make hay while the son
    shines!

A farmer was driving along the road with a load of
fertilizer. A child playing in front of his house saw him
and called, "What are you hauling?"

"Fertilizer," the farmer replied.

"What are you going to do with it?" asked the child.

"Put it on strawberries," answered the farmer.

"You ought to live here," the child advised him. "We
put sugar and cream on them."

Some cowboys were sitting around a campfire telling
stories. One of them said, "I know an Indian who never
forgets anything. The Devil can have my soul if I'm not
telling the truth."

That night the Devil appeared and said, "Come along
with me."

"I was telling the truth," the cowpoke replied. "I'll
show you."

The two of them went to the Indian. "Do you like
eggs?" the Devil asked.

"Yes," the Indian replied.

Then the cowboy and the Devil went away. Twenty
years later, the Devil heard that the cowboy had died,
and he went off to find the Indian.

"How!" the Devil said, greeting him Indian-style with
his right arm raised.

"Fried," the Indian answered.

A salesman parked his foreign sports car in front of the general store. When he came out of the store, a farmer was looking the car over. "Well, how do you like it?" asked the salesman. The farmer replied, "Picked it before it was ripe, didn't you?"

First Cowboy: Why are you wearing only one spur?
Second Cowboy: Well, I figure when one side of the horse starts running, the other side will too.

Farmer: This is a dogwood tree.
Tourist: How can you tell?
Farmer: By its bark.

Parachuter (who had just landed in a tree): I was trying to make a new record.

Farmer: You did. You're the first man ever to climb down from that tree before he climbed up.

Ma and Pa Eli were coming down from the mountain when they saw a motorcycle zoom by. Pa Eli, who had never seen one before, took quick aim with his squirrel gun and fired.

"Kill it, Pa?" Ma Eli asked.

"Naw, it's still growling, but I sure made it let go of that man it had."

Some city boys were hiking in the country. One of them came upon a pile of empty milk bottles and called excitedly to his companions, "Come quick. I've found a cow's nest!"

In the mood for joking, a vacationer strolled over to a farmer working in a field and asked, "Did you happen to see a wagonload of monkeys go by?"

"Nope," replied the farmer. "Did you fall off?"

A cowboy on a dude ranch watched one of the guests trying to saddle a horse. "Pardon me," he said politely, "but you're putting the saddle on backwards."

"What makes you so sure?" the guest asked angrily. "You don't even know in which direction I'm going."

Sid from the city: What do you do with the fruit around here?

Farmer: We eat what we can, and what we can't, we can!

A tourist driving through New Hampshire wasn't sure he was on the right road, so he asked a farmer on a tractor, "Which way is it to Rutledge, please?"

"Don't know," the farmer answered.

"Well, then, which way is it to Hanover?" the tourist asked.

"Don't know," the farmer repeated.

The tourist snapped, "Don't you know anything?"

"Well," the farmer replied, "I ain't lost."

FAMOUS FIGURES

Question: If kings like to sit on gold, who likes to sit on
   silver?
Answer: The Lone Ranger.

Ted: Do you believe in fate?

Fred: I don't know, why?

Ted: Well, did you ever wonder why famous men were all born on holidays?

Teacher: Robert, tell me something about Christopher Columbus.

Robert: He was the explorer who discovered America. And he was very economical.

Teacher: Economical?

Robert: Yes. He was the only man to travel thirty thousand miles on a galleon.

Teacher: Tom, who was the smartest inventor of all time?

Tom: Edison. He invented the phonograph and radio so people would stay up all night and use his electric light bulbs.

A Princeton neighbor of Professor Albert Einstein became concerned because her young daughter made it a practice to visit the famed scientist every afternoon. The mother apologized to Einstein for her daughter's constant interruptions of his scientific endeavors.

"Oh, not at all," Einstein reassured her. "I enjoy her visits, and we get along very well."

"But what can you and an eight-year-old girl have in common?" asked the mother.

"A great deal," Einstein explained. "I love the jelly beans she brings me, and she loves the way I do her arithmetic lessons."

Sherlock Holmes, the master detective, was sitting in his study smoking his pipe and reading when there was a knock on the door, and his friend and assistant Dr. Watson entered.

"Good day, Watson," said the detective. "Don't you think it is a bit warm to be wearing your red flannel underwear?"

"What an amazing bit of detection and deduction, Holmes!" exclaimed Watson. "But how on earth did you know that I am still wearing my red flannel underwear?"

"Elementary, my dear Watson," said Holmes. "You've forgotten to put on your trousers!"

Two flies were standing on Robinson Crusoe's knee.

"Good-by for now," said one of them. "I'll be seeing you on Friday."

Bill: Did you know you can't send mail to Washington?
Jill: No, why not?
Bill: Because he's dead. But you can send mail to Lincoln.
Jill: But he's dead too.
Bill: I know, but he left his Gettysburg Address.

The teacher called on little Joey. "Tell me what you know about George Washington. Was he a soldier or a sailor?"

"I think he was a soldier," replied Joey.

"Why do you say that?"

"I saw a picture of him when he was crossing the Delaware, and any sailor knows enough not to stand up in a rowboat."

An Irish potato married an Idaho potato, and they had a little baby spud. When the sweet girl potato was ready to be married, she announced to her father, "Dad, I want to marry Chet Huntley." Her father was indignant. "Absolutely not, my dear. He's just a commentator."

Barry: Gee, I never knew Charles Dickens wrote music.
Carry: Neither did I. What did he write?
Barry: *Oliver Twist*.

Once two boys decided to play a trick on the great naturalist Charles Darwin. Very carefully they glued together parts of several insects, including a butterfly's wings, a bee's head, and a grasshopper's legs. Then they took their creation to the famous man and asked, "What kind of bug is this?"

"Did it hum when you caught it?" Darwin asked them.

The boys, feeling certain they had fooled the scientist, said, "Yes!"

"That's just as I thought," Darwin replied. "It's a humbug."

A man from Boston had spent an entire evening listening to a Texan brag about the heroes of the Alamo. Finally the Texan said, "I'll bet you never had anyone that brave in Boston."

"Have you ever heard of Paul Revere?" asked the Bostonian.

"Paul Revere?" said the Texan. "Oh, yes. Wasn't he the fellow who ran for help?"

Benjamin Franklin may have discovered electricity, but the man who invented the meter made all the money.

Mike: Did you know that Teddy Roosevelt was mean to horses?
Ike: Yes. He was a Rough Rider.

Shakespeare: I've written a new play, but I think the title is too long.

Miss Hathaway: What is it?

Shakespeare: It's *Julius, Grab the Girl Quickly Before She Gets Away*.

Miss Hathaway: Why not just call it *Julius Caesar*?

Question: What kind of corsage did Lassie wear to the ball?

Answer: A collie flower.

Question: Why couldn't anyone find the famous composer?

Answer: Because he was Haydn.

Ron: Why did Mickey Mouse go on a trip to outer space?

John: I don't know. Why?

Ron: Because he wanted to find Pluto.

Question: What did Benjamin Franklin say when he discovered electricity in lightning?

Answer: Nothing. He was too shocked.

Romeo: Juliet, dearest, I'm burning with love for you.

Juliet: Come, now, Romeo, don't make a fuel of yourself.

INSULTS AND WISECRACKS

Terry: Say something soft and sweet.
Jerry: Marshmallow.

An antelope watching a kangaroo with a baby in its pouch remarked: "What does she think she is, a backward Indian?"

Clara: Whenever I'm in the dumps, I get a new hat.
Sarah: Oh, so that's where you get them!

Bert: You remind me of the ocean.

Gert: Romantic, wild, and restless?

Bert: No, you just make me sick.

An impatient passenger stopped a porter in a bus terminal. "Where do I get the three o'clock bus for New York, my good man?" he asked.

The porter pointed. "Turn left and you'll be right."

"Don't get fresh with me!" the passenger warned him.

"Of course not, sir. Turn right and you'll be left."

Postmaster: Here's your five-cent stamp.

Shopper (with arms full of bundles): Do I have to stick it on myself?

Postmaster: Nope. On the envelope.

Catty: Did you hear what happened to Hazel when she went to the movies?

Matty: No, what?

Catty: The usher had to ask her to take off her hair.

Catty: Was she embarrassed when they asked her to take off her mask at the masquerade party!

Matty: Why?

Catty: She wasn't wearing one.

Question: What does a pregnant lady drink right before she's about to have twins?

Answer: Schaeffer—it's the one beer to have when you're having more than one.

Lady (standing in the middle of the street): Officer, can you tell me how to get to the hospital from here?

Policeman: Just stand right where you are.

Harry: My father is an Elk, a Lion, and a Moose.

Larry: How much does it cost to see him?

Pete: You dance very well.

Pam: I wish I could say the same for you.

Pete: You could if you were as big a liar as I am.

Gary: Your sister is sure spoiled, isn't she?
Barry: No, that's just the perfume she's wearing.

Jim: I feel sorry for Johnny.
Tim: Why?
Jim: The only way he can hear any good about himself
    is to talk to himself.

Ron: He reminds me of Whistler's mother standing up.
Don: Why do you say that?
Ron: He's off his rocker!

Ray: People call him the wonder boy.
Kay: They do?
Ray: Yes, they look at him and wonder.

Lady (to passing stranger): Can you tell me how to get
to Carnegie Hall?
Stranger: By hard work.

Rude Boy on a Blind Date: You could make a good
living hiring yourself out to haunt houses.

Read in the will of a miserly millionaire: ". . . and to
my dear brother Fred, whom I promised to remember
in my will, 'Hi there, Fred!'"

He's such a blockhead, he gets a splinter in his fingers
every time he scratches his head.

He looks about as comfortable as a centipede with
athlete's foot.

He's a second-story man. No one ever believes his first
story.

He's not really two-faced. If he had two, why would he
be wearing that one?

He might as well blow his brains out. He's got nothing
to lose.

They call him "chocolate bar." He's half nuts.

His speeches go over like a pregnant woman trying to
pole vault.

Boy to Girl: Gosh, I was going to buy you some new handkerchiefs, but I forgot the size of your nose.

Ann: Joe reminds me of a cloudy day.

Dan: Why do you say that?

Ann: The closest he'll ever come to a brainstorm is a light drizzle.

Monica: I told Nancy that brains aren't everything.

Veronica: Why did you say that?

Monica: Because in her case they're nothing.

Al: Do you think Joe's very smart?

Sal: Well, they say he has a photographic memory. The trouble is, nothing seems to develop.

Tina: I have a feeling my goldfish is very intelligent. How can I communicate with him?

Nina: Drop him a line.

Rick: If I saw a man beating a donkey and made him stop, what virtue would I be showing?

Dick: Brotherly love.

Penny: Have you heard the one about the bed?

Benny: No, I haven't.

Penny: No wonder. It hasn't been made up yet.

If I've said anything to insult you, believe me, I've tried my best.

John: I throw myself into everything I undertake.

Don: Go dig a deep well.

Ray: Our dog is just like one of the family.

Fay: Really? Which one?

Barry: What do you think of Susie?

Larry: She's smart—a regular encyclopedia. One thing she doesn't know though—reference books are never taken out.

Offer him a penny for his thoughts and you're being more than generous.

Take some friendly advice. Send your wits out to be sharpened.

Sam: Fred reminds me of a fence.
Pam: Why do you say that?
Sam: He runs around a lot but never gets anywhere.

Jed: She sure gave you a dirty look.
Ted: Who?
Jed: Mother Nature!

Will: Did anyone laugh when you fell on the ice?
Jill: No, but the ice made some awful cracks.

George was playing the piano for his friend Sidney.

"Well, how do you like it?" George asked.

"You should be on the radio," Sidney said.

"You mean I'm that good?"

"No," George answered. "Then I could turn you off."

Tim: I've changed my mind.

Jim: Thank goodness! Does the new one work any better?

Pat: You know, George spends half his time trying to be witty.

Matt: Yes. You might say he's a half-wit.

Arty: The tornado that blew my father's car away left another in its place.

Smarty: Must have been a trade wind.

Scientists often wonder whether the splitting of the atom was a wise crack.

Ed: You have the manners of a gentleman.

Fred (looking pleased): Why, thank you.

Ed: Tell me, to whom do they belong?

Host: We'd love to have you stay here tonight, but you will have to make your own bed.

Guest: That's fine with me.

Host: Good. Here's a hammer, saw, and some nails.

NUTS AT THE WHEEL

Question: What kind of song do you sing in a car?
Answer: A cartoon!

A motorist was going down a one-way street the wrong way.
Policeman: Do you know where you are going?
Motorist: Yes, but I must be late. Everyone else is coming back.

Sue: What is the best thing to take when you are run down?
Lou: The license number of the car that hit you.

Traffic Cop: When I saw you driving down the highway, I said, "Sixty-five at least."

Woman Driver: Well, you're wrong, officer. It's just this hat that makes me look older.

Husband (surveying dents in his new car): You must think autos grow on trees.

Wife: Not at all. Everybody knows they come from plants.

Doorman: Your car is at the door, sir.

Car Owner: Yes, I hear it knocking.

Sign in front of a gas station: PUT A TIGER IN YOUR TANK. Sign on another gas station a mile down the road:

OUR FINE FILTERS REMOVE TIGER HAIRS.

Question: At what time of day are you like an automobile wheel?

Answer: At night when you are tired.

Phil: How can you tell a happy motorcyclist?

Bill: I don't know.

Phil: By the number of bugs on his teeth.

Question: What do you call a person who steals motorbikes?

Answer: A Honda-taker.

Fred: Why does a Model-T Ford remind you of a
schoolroom?

Ted: Because it has a lot of little nuts, with a crank up
front.

Question: What kind of driver never gets arrested?
Answer: A screw-driver.

Long, long ago an old Indian chief was about to die, so
he called for Geronimo and Falling Rocks, the two
bravest warriors in his tribe. The chief instructed each
to go out and seek buffalo skins. Whoever returned
with the most skins would be chief. About a month
later Geronimo came back with one hundred pelts, but
Falling Rocks never returned. Even today as you drive
throughout the West you can see signs saying: WATCH
OUT FOR FALLING ROCKS.

Professor: I say there, you in the automobile. Your
tubular air container has lost its rotundity.

Driver: Huh?

Professor: I said the cylindrical apparatus which sup-
ports your vehicle is no longer symmetrical.

Driver: Wha . . . ?

Professor: The elastic fabric surrounding the circular
frame whose successive revolutions bear you on-
ward in space has not retained its pristine rotundity.

Driver: Which?

Passing Boy: Hey, mister, he says you got a flat tire.

A lady driving on Highway 89 was racing along at eighty-nine miles an hour when a policeman stopped her. "Madam, why were you going so fast?"

"Well," the lady replied, "I saw the sign back there that said '89,' and I was just going the speed limit."

The cop sighed. "It's a good thing I caught you before you got to Highway 201."

Auto manufacturers are naming many of their new models after sea creatures. There are the Sting Ray, the Barracuda, the Marlin, and so on. Volkswagen will probably have to follow suit by making a smaller bus and calling it the "Polliwogen."

An alarmed motorist quickly pulled his car to a stop when he saw a young man standing beside an overturned sports car.

"Anybody injured in the accident?" he inquired.

"No accident," assured the young man, "I'm just changing a flat."

Driving Instructor: Now, tell me. What would you do
if your brakes suddenly failed to work?
Student: I'd try to hit something cheap.

Question: What did the jack say to the car?
Answer: Can I give you a lift?

Ned: I've owned this car for ten years and never had a
wreck.
Fred: What you mean is that you've owned this wreck
for ten years and never had a car.

Question: What part of the car is the cause of most
accidents?
Answer: The nut that holds the wheel!

A Mathematics professor complained to the policeman
that a driver had almost run him down as he tried to
cross the street.

"Were you able to get his license number?" the
policeman asked.

"Well, not exactly," the professor said. "But I do
remember noticing that if it was doubled and then
multiplied by itself, the square root of the product was
the original number with the integers reversed."

Garage Attendant: Is your horn broken?
Customer: No, it doesn't care.
Garage Attendant: What do you mean?
Customer: It doesn't give a hoot.

Bud: What's the difference between a book of fiction
    and the red light of a car?
Dud: I have no idea.
Bud: One is a light tale and the other is a tail light.

Pedestrian (lying in the road): What's the matter with
    you, are you blind?
Driver: What do you mean, blind? I hit you, didn't I?

Mack: All this talk about backseat driving is hogwash.
    I've driven for fifteen years and I've never heard
    a word from back there.
Jack: What kind of car do you drive?
Mack: A hearse.

Sign in a Police Station: IT TAKES APPROXIMATELY
3500 BOLTS TO PUT AN AUTOMOBILE TOGETHER BUT
ONLY ONE NUT TO SCATTER IT ALL OVER THE ROAD.

Teacher: What is an autobiography?
Student: Er—the life story of an automobile.

Sign in a Volkswagen factory: THINK BIG—and you're
fired.

Question: Why can't a bicycle stand up by itself?
Answer: Because it is two-tired.

Dean: How do you top a car?
Keen: 'Tep on the brake, 'tupid.

Driver: My car just went under some quicksand.
Insurance Agent: That's all right. Don't worry about
    it.
Driver: Why not?
Insurance Agent: Your car is completely covered.

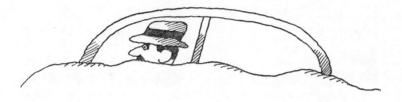

Question: What age is most important to an auto-
    mobile?
Answer: Mileage.

A man was driving down a one-way street the wrong
way when he was stopped by a policeman. "This is a
one-way street," the officer said. "I know," the man
replied, "I'm only going one way."

After a long day's drive over winding roads through
the White Mountains of New Hampshire, a tourist was
stopped by a state policeman.

"I'll have to give you a ticket for driving without a
tail light," the policeman said.

The tourist stepped out of his car and gave a cry of
despair. "It's not as bad as all that," said the policeman.

The tourist replied, "I'm not worried about the ticket.
But where's my trailer?"

Jed: Do you need a license to drive a car on the road?

Ted: Yes.

Jed: Do you need a license to ride a horse on the road?

Ted: No.

Jed: Then you don't need a license to drive a car on the road.

Ted: Why?

Jed: Because cars run on horse-power.

Judge: Now tell me, why did you park your car here?

Motorist: Well, there was a sign that said FINE FOR PARKING.

HIPPIES, HAIRDOS, AND HERMITS

Rusty: What would you have if you crossed the Beatles
   and the trash men?
Dusty: I don't know.
Rusty: Litterbugs.

Rusty: If the head of the U.S. is called the President and the head of England is the Prime Minister, what is the head of Nova Scotia called?

Dusty: I don't know. What?

Rusty: The Bossa Nova.

Question: Why isn't Beatle Bubble Bath Powder any good?

Answer: Because it leaves a Ringo around your bathtub.

Pop: I can't understand why boys grow their hair so long these days.

Hippie: Well, Jefferson and Washington had pretty long hair, too.

Pop: Yes, but they didn't go around strumming guitars to call attention to it.

A hippie was driving down a one-way street the wrong way. A policeman stopped him.

Policeman: Didn't you see the arrow?

Hippie: Like man, I didn't see the Indian.

Two hippies went into a restaurant. The owner stopped them at the door and said, "You must wear a tie to be seated in this restaurant." One hippie left and returned a little later wearing a tie.

The restaurant owner pointed to the other one and asked, "What about him?"

"Him?" replied the tie-wearer. "That's my wife!"

Dash: What did the pants say to the blouse as they tumbled around in the washing machine?

Tide: Meet me at the clothesline; that's where I hang out.

A visitor to the Modern Art Museum examined an object of art and then remarked to a guard standing nearby, "And this, I suppose, is one of those hideous representations you call modern art."

"No, lady," replied the guard. "That's called a mirror."

Hip: Can you do the Mouse, the Frug, or the Watusi?

Pip: No, but I can do that new dance called the elevator.

Hip: How do you do that?

Pip: Here's how it goes—no steps.

After spending an afternoon on Fifth Avenue, a male observer decided that what goes on in the average beauty shop today is simply hair-raising.

Question: What did the boy octopus say to the girl octopus?

Answer: I want to hold your hand hand hand hand hand hand hand hand.

Teeny Bopper: Pop, what should I wear with my yellow-and-orange checkered knee socks?

Pop: Hip boots!

Question: What did the cricket say to the beetle?
Answer: Bug, you *man* me!

Did you hear about the two hippies who hired a woman to come in every week and dirty up?

Question: Why did the hippie go to the barbershop?
Answer: Because he couldn't stand his hair any longer.

Jennifer and Gerald were walking by a theater and saw a sign which said: NEXT ATTRACTION—ENGLAND'S TOP GROUPS: THE ANIMALS, THE ZOMBIES, THE HERMITS, THE ROLLING STONES, THE KINKS.
Gerald to Jennifer: Are you sure it's a rock-'n'-roll show and not a monster rally?

Rusty: What's black and white and has fuzz inside?
Dusty: A police car.

Question: How can you tell when you're too old to do the Monkey?
Answer: When your a-go-go is a-gone-gone.

Question: What would you have if Batman and Robin were run over by a steam roller?
Answer: Flatman and Ribbon.

Question: What is Batman's favorite sport?
Answer: Batminton.

Question: Why was Batman sad in the autumn?
Answer: Because Robin flew South.

Two hippies were on a space flight. As they passed by the rings of the planet Saturn, one turned to the other and said, "Look at those crazy hula-hoops!"

Rusty: Who is that guy with the long hair?
Dusty: He's the sophomore from Yale.
Rusty: Oh, I've often heard of those Yale locks.

Question: Why did the old lady put wheels on her rocking chair?
Answer: Because she wanted to rock 'n' roll.

ALL IN THE FAMILY

Father: Son, if you don't stop strumming that guitar, I'll go out of my mind.
Son: It's too late, Dad. I stopped playing an hour ago.

Mrs. Busy: Did you meet your son at the airport?
Mrs. Body: Oh, goodness, no! I've known him for years.

Father: Johnny, you're a pig. Do you know what a pig is?
Johnny: Sure, Pop. A pig is a hog's little boy.

Ron: Why did the boy's mother call him Sonny?
Don: I don't know, why?
Ron: Because he was so bright.

Benny: How did Mom find out you didn't really take a bath?
Denny: I forgot to wet the soap.

Oliver: Mother, will you do my arithmetic for me?
Mother: No, Oliver, it wouldn't be right.
Oliver: Well, at least you could try.

Mother: Sit down and tell me what your school grades are.
Son: I can't sit down. I just told Dad.

Mother: What do you want to take your cod liver oil with today?
Sammy: With a fork.

Barry: Did your mother ever lift weights?
Harry: No, why?
Barry: How did she raise a dumb-bell like you?

Sarah: My bird can talk, Mother.

Mother: Really?

Sarah: Yes. I asked her what is two minus two, and she said nothing.

Mother: Ellen, why are you making faces at that bull-dog?

Ellen (wailing): He started it.

Mother Lion: Son, what are you doing?

Baby Lion: I'm chasing a hunter around a tree.

Mother Lion: How often do I have to tell you not to play with your food.

Ed: What is brown or black and leaves you black and
    blue?
Ted: I don't know. What?
Ed: Your father's belt.

Mother: Where are you going, Freddie?
Freddie: I'm going out to watch a solar eclipse.
Mother: All right, dear, but don't get too close.

A father who wants his children to get an education
these days may have to pull a few wires: the television
wire, the telephone wire, the stereo wire, and the radio
wire.

Jimmy: Dad, did you ever hear a rabbit bark?
Dad: Of course not. Rabbits don't bark!
Jimmy: But my teacher told us that rabbits eat cabbage
    and bark.

Mother: When that naughty boy threw stones at you,
    why didn't you come and tell me, instead of throw-
    ing them back at him?
Son: What good would it do to tell you? You couldn't
    hit the side of a garage.

Teddy: Say, Ma, how much am I worth to you?
Mother: Why, you're worth a million to me, dear.
Teddy: Well, then, could you advance me a quarter?

Mother: Johnny, I was hoping you would be unselfish enough to give your little sister the largest piece of candy. Why even a hen gives all the best pieces of food to her chicks and takes only a small piece now and then for herself.

Johnny: Sure, Mom, I'd do the same thing if it were worms.

Mother: Why do you want to keep this bag of dirt, Albert?

Albert: It's instant mudpie mix.

Dad (looking suspiciously at the dessert his daughter has whipped up): What's this, Nancy?

Nancy: It's cottage pudding. We learned how to make it at school today.

Dad: Well, I think I got a piece of shingle in my mouth.

Little Johnny was raking leaves with his father, who was telling him about what made leaves turn brown. Suddenly the boy turned to his father and said: "What's all this about little fairies turning the leaves? Hasn't anyone ever heard of the process of photosynthesis?"

Mack: How's your father coming with his new dairy farm?

Jack: He makes all the cows sleep on their backs.

Mack: What's the idea?

Jack: It's so the cream will be on top in the morning.

Father: Well, Bob, how are your marks?
Bob: They're under water.
Father: What does that mean?
Bob: Below *C* level.

Big Brother: Know how I keep my head above water?
Little Brother: Sure. Wood floats!

Uncle (to little Johnny): What would you like to be
    when you grow up?
Johnny: A vitamin.
Uncle: How can you be a vitamin?
Johnny: I don't know, but I saw a sign in the drugstore
    window that said VITAMIN B-1!

"Mother," said little Ricky, "today our teacher asked me whether or not I had any brothers or sisters, and I told her I was an only child."

"And what did she say?" asked his mother.

"Thank goodness," Ricky replied.

Father: Ron, why is your January report card so bad?
Ron: You know how it is, Pop. Things are always marked down after Christmas.

Proud Mother: Baby Ben is a year old now and he's been walking since he was eight months old.
Bored Listener: Really? He must be awfully tired.

Father was showing Billy the family album and came across a picture of himself and his wife on their wedding day.

"Was that the day Mom came to work for us?" Billy asked.

Off to school for the first time, little Janey was given her birth certificate in an envelope and told by her mother not to lose it.

That afternoon Janey came home crying. When her mother asked her what was wrong, she announced, "I lost my excuse for being born!"

Doctor: How is your sister getting along with her reducing diet?
Tommy: Just fine—she disappeared last week!

A mother pigeon was exasperated with one of her squabs which was scared to fly. The mother laid down an ultimatum. "Either you learn to fly today or I'll tie a string on you and tow you." "But, Mother," protested the little pigeon, "I don't want to be a pigeon towed."

Father: Denny's teacher says he ought to have an encyclopedia.
Mother: Let him walk to school like I did.

Randy: Which is bigger: Mr. Bigger or Mr. Bigger's baby?
Andy: I don't know. Which?
Randy: The baby is a little Bigger.

Penny: Mother, what was the name of the last station our train stopped at?
Mother: Don't bother me; I don't know. Can't you see I'm reading?
Penny: Well, it's too bad you don't know, because Little Brother got off there.

Question: Why is the letter *D* like a bad boy?
Answer: Because it makes Ma mad.

Big Brother (to the clerk in the store): My mother wants a dozen diapers for the new baby.
Clerk: Here they are. That will be five dollars for the diapers and fifteen cents for the tax.
Big Brother: Don't bother about the tacks. My mother uses safety pins.

Freddie: Do you think anyone can predict the future with cards?

Teddie: My mother can. She took one look at my report card and told me exactly what would happen when Dad got home!

Harry: My uncle disappeared when he was on a safari in Africa.

Larry: What happened to him?

Harry: Pop says that something he disagreed with ate him.

Mother: Stu, did you fall down with your good pants on?

Stu: Yes, Mommy, there wasn't time to take them off.

Ricky: Mom, I need a new jacket.

Mom: Ricky, your horsehide jacket is only a month old and nearly worn out!

Ricky: Yeah, Mom, but look how long the horse wore it.

Connie: I found a horseshoe, Mother.

Mother: Do you know what that means?

Connie: Yes, Mother, some poor horse is running around in his stocking feet.

Jim went with his mother to the store. The grocer gave him an apple. "What do you say to Mr. Jones, Jim?" his mother said. "Peel it, please," Jim replied.

Father and son were posing for a picture following the son's graduation from college. "Stand closer to your father. Try to look a little more natural," the photographer said. "I think he'd look more natural," the father replied, "if he stood with his hands in my pockets."

A little planet broke out of orbit and raced around the sun and moon. His mother called, "What are you doing, son?" "Look, Mom," shouted the little planet, "no gravities!"

Mother: Stop asking so many questions. Don't you know that curiosity killed the cat?

Sally: Really? What did the cat want to know?

Little Larry: Ma, may I have a nickel for the old lady who is outside crying?

Mother: Yes, dear, but what is the old lady crying about?

Larry: She's crying, "Salty peanuts, five cents a bag."

Johnny rushed out of the bathroom. "Oh, Mother," he shouted, "I saw something running across the floor with no legs."

"Nonsense," said his mother. "What are you talking about?"

"Water," was the reply.

Son: Dad, what is a weapon?

Father: Why, son, that's something you fight with.

Son: Is mother your weapon?

Pat: What are five peaches plus three peaches?

Pop: Add five peaches to three peaches. Don't you know the answer? Haven't you ever done a problem like this before?

Pat: No. In school we added apples.

Father: You aren't talking in class anymore, are you?

Pammy: Not any more—just the same amount.

A hard-working farmer and his son had saved all their lives so that the boy could go to college. After he had gone for about a year, he came home for Christmas, and his father wanted to know something that he had learned there. So, the boy said, "πR^2." His father yelled, "Son, do you mean to tell me that pies are square? You know right well that pies are round. Corn bread is square."

A boy away at school sent a cable to his father asking for money. This is what it said: "No mon, no fun, your son." The reply came back: "How sad, too bad, your dad!"

Linda: Mother, is it correct to say that you water your horse?

Mother: Yes, dear.

Linda: Then I'm going out to milk my cat.

Mother brought Tommy into the barbershop, dressed like a cowboy and brandishing his toy six-shooter. He scrambled into the barber's chair, and shouted, "Bang, bang, bang!"

"I'll be back in half an hour," his mother told the barber. "I've got some errands to do."

"I hope the boy doesn't get too restless," the barber said, worriedly.

"Oh, if he does," she replied, "just drop dead for him a few times."

Barber: Well, Bobby, how would you like your hair cut?

Bobby: Just like Pop's, and be sure to leave that little round hole on the top where his head comes through.

Franky: Dad, how long does it take to get from New York to Boston?

Dad: Four hours.

Franky: How long from Boston to New York?

Dad: The same. You ought to know that.

Franky: Well, it's not the same from Thanksgiving to Christmas as it is from Christmas to Thanksgiving.

Mrs. Smith had invited the boss and his wife for dinner, and Becky was given the job of setting the table. But when it came time to eat, Becky's mother said with surprise, "Why didn't you give Mrs. Covington a knife and fork, dear?"

"I didn't think I needed to," Becky explained. "I heard Daddy say she always eats like a horse."

Brave Young Bob: I've come to ask for your daughter's hand.
Father: You'll have to take all of her, or it's no deal.

A father took his young son to the opera for the first time. The conductor started waving the baton, and the soprano began her aria. The boy watched everything intently and finally asked: "Why is he hitting her with his stick?"

"He's not hitting her," answered the father with a chuckle.

"Well, then," asked the boy, "why is she screaming?"

Candy: I'm not going to school anymore.
Mother: Why, what do you mean?
Candy: On Monday the teacher said five and five makes ten. On Tuesday she said six and four makes ten. Today she said seven and three makes ten. I'm not going back to school again until she makes up her mind!

Father: Well, son, how do you like school?
Son: Closed!

Timmy's mother sent him to the store. When he got back, she called the grocer and said angrily, "I ordered four pounds of apples, and you only sent me three!"

"Lady," the grocer replied, "my scales are correct. But have you weighed your son?"

Sammy: Pop, what's radioactivity?

Father (hemming and hawing): Well, I'm afraid I don't really know much about atomic energy.

Sammy (a little later): How do space satellites orbit?

Father: I guess I don't know much about space technology either.

Sammy (still later): Dad, how does a jet take off?

Father: It's too complicated to explain.

Sammy: I guess I'm bothering you.

Father: Of course not. You have to ask questions if you want to learn anything.

Phil: My mom treats me like an idol.

Bill: Why do you say that?

Phil: She feeds me burnt offerings at meals.

Mr. Prince saw a group of boys gathered around a small cat. His son Tommy was in the group.

"What are you doing?" asked Mr. Prince.

"Trading lies," said Tommy. "The one who tells the biggest lie gets the kitten."

"Why, when I was your age, I never thought of telling lies," said Mr. Prince.

"Okay, you win, Mr. Prince. The cat's yours," cried one of the boys.

Mandy: Mother, there's a delivery man here with a package for you.

Mother: What is it, dear?

Mandy: He says it's fish, and it's marked C.O.D.

Mother: Tell him to take it back, dear. I ordered halibut.

Little Linda was going to church for the first time. As she was leaving with her parents, the minister asked how she had liked church. "I liked the music," she replied, "but the commercial was too long."

Wendy: Mom, do you remember that plate you always worried I would break?

Mother: Yes, what about it?

Wendy: Your worries are over.

Mandy: My grandfather has a wooden leg.

Candy: Well, my grandmother has a cedar chest.

Salesman: Young man, is your mother at home?

Freddy: Yes, sir.

Salesman (after knocking for some time and getting no answer): I thought you said she was home.

Freddy: Yes sir, but we don't live here.

Mother: Jimmy, how did I happen to catch you with your hand in the cookie jar?

Jimmy: I guess it was because I didn't hear you coming.

Mother: Harold, why is your face so red?

Harold: I was running up the street to stop a fight.

Mother: That's a very gentlemanly thing to do. Who was fighting?

Harold: Me and another boy.

Mother: Come in, Susie, and I'll give you some milk and cookies. Are your feet dirty?

Susie: Yes, Mother, but I've got my shoes on.

Mother: Everything is going up. The price of food is going up. The price of clothing is going up. I wish there was one thing that was going down.

Nancy: Here's my report card, Mom. I think it will make you feel better.

Mother: Were you a good girl at church today, Susie?

Susie: I sure was. A nice man offered me a whole plate full of money, and I said, "No, thank you."

It was spring and Mr. Corley called the telephone company to order a fifty-foot extension cord put on the phone. He explained: "Now that spring is here and the weather is nice, I want my daughter to stay outdoors more."

DONE WITH A PUN

First Dolphin: What did you say when you bumped into that bully dolphin?
Second Dolphin: I just told him I didn't do it on por- poise!

Sam: Why did the chicken cross the road?
Pam: For fowl reasons.

Bill: Do you know another name for a smart duck?
Jill: I'd call him a wise quacker.

Don: Did you hear about the awful row in the dime
store last night?
Ron: No, what happened?
Don: Two suckers got licked.

Mr. Handy was putting up a knotty pine wall in his
living room. His young son came along and said, "What
are those holes for?"

"They're *knot* holes," replied the father.

"Well, then," said the boy, "if they're not holes, what
are they?"

Mother moth was astonished to see baby moth crying.
"Stop that at once," she commanded. "This is the first
time I've ever seen a moth bawl."

Ted: What did the doughnut say to the rolls?
Ned: If I had as much dough as you have, I sure
wouldn't be hanging around this hole.

Did you hear about the chicken that stopped halfway
across the road? She wanted to lay it on the line.

Bo: Where do you live?
Joe: On Minute Street.
Bo: I never heard of that one.
Joe: Oh. Well, it's usually called Sixty-second Street.

Harry: What happened when the sea gull flew out and landed on a channel marker?

Barry: It was a case of buoy meets gull.

Jim: Do you know the story about the mountain?

Tim: No, I don't.

Jim: Forget it; it's all a bluff.

Tom: What did the Pueblo boy say when his dog fell over a cliff?

Ted: Why, *"Doggone,"* of course!

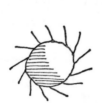

Romeo (as he threw stones into the stream): I am merely a pebble in your life.

Juliet: Why don't you try being a little boulder.

Jane: What colors would you paint the sun and the wind?

June: I'd say, the sun rose and the wind blue.

Rod: What did one casket say to the other casket?

Tod: I don't know.

Rod: Is that you coffin?

Judge (to prisoner): Name, occupation, and charge.

Prisoner: My name is Sparks; my occupation is Electricity; the charge is Battery.

A group of brave souls were having their first lesson in sky diving.

"What if the chute doesn't open?" asked one.

"That," said the instructor grimly, "is what we call jumping to a conclusion."

Question: Why did the three little pigs decide to leave home?

Answer: They thought their father was an awful boar.

Have you heard about the two buckets who were conversing at the fountain?

"You're a little pail," said one.

"Yes," replied the other, "I'm not a well bucket."

Question: Why was the library sad?
Answer: Because the books were in tiers.

Sam: We have a new baby in our house.
Pam: I bet he reigns as king in your family now.
Sam: No—Prince of Wails.

Jim: Do you know how to make a slow horse fast?
Tim: Nope, do you?
Jim: Just don't give him anything to eat.

Ted: Do you know how many days belong to the year?
Fred: All of them, I suppose.
Ted: Nope, just 325. The rest are Lent.

Stu: How far can a spook travel?
Sue: From ghost to ghost.

Len: What happens to little girls who eat bullets?
Glen: Their hair grows out in bangs.

Lou: Do you know Art?
Sue: Art who?
Lou: Artesian.
Sue: Sure. I know artesian well.

Steve: Have you heard what the sea said to the shore?
Eve: No, what?
Steve: Nothing. It just waved.

"Where did I come from?" asked the baby ear of corn.
"The stalk brought you," answered its mother.

Penny: My father can play the piano by ear.
Benny: That's nothing. My father fiddles with his
whiskers.

Ef: The other day I heard about a man who ate ten
dozen pancakes.
Jeff: Oh, how waffle!

First Thief: How did you get away from the blood-
hounds?

Second Thief: I threw a penny into the woods and they
followed the wrong cent.

Sal: Why didn't the little boys mind the baby sitter?

Val: I don't know, why?

Sal: Because she was supposed to mind them.

Sherlock: Why did the secret agent talk into the hair
drier?

Shelly: I don't know. Why?

Sherlock: Because it was a shortwave radio.

Question: What is the teapot's favorite song?

Answer: "Home on the Range."

Al: Did you hear about the fight at the bus terminal?

Sal: No, how did it start?

Al: The tickets got punched.

Mike: Why did you title your first movie "The Broken
Arm?"

Ike: Because it had a big cast.

Realtor: Now here is a perfect house. It doesn't have a
flaw.

Bostonian: But what do you walk on?

Bob: Why is the nose in the middle of the face?
Rob: Because it's the scenter.

There once was an Indian chief whose name was Shortcake. He lived in the mountains with his wife, Squaw.
One day Shortcake died, and a sympathetic Indian
asked Squaw what she would do with him. She answered sadly, "Squaw bury Shortcake."

Question: What's worse than raining cats and dogs?
Answer: Hailing taxis.

Mrs. Clean decided she wanted to take a milk bath, so she asked the milkman for ten gallons of milk.

"Do you want it pasteurized?" the milkman asked.

"No," replied Mrs. Clean, "up to my knees will be fine."

"Mine is all write," chuckled the author.

"Ours is pretty light," commented the electrician.

"My business is looking up," said the astronomer.

"Mine is looking better," bragged the optician.

"Mine is just sew, sew," remarked the seamstress.

"Mine is picking up," smiled the chamber maid.

"Mine is growing," boasted the farmer.

"Mine is going up in smoke," complained the cigarette-maker.

A teacher asked her class to use each of a series of words in a sentence. These are the responses she received:

Laziness—It's no wonder baby doesn't get tired, he laziness crib all day.

Avenue—I avenue baby sister.

Butter—She wanted to go, butter mother wouldn't let her.

Shiver—I lost Mamma's watch, and she'll be awful mad if shiver finds out.

Lilac—He's a good kid, but he can lilac anything.

Wiggle—She wears her hat all the time because she's afraid her wiggle come off.

Bulletin—Pa got in a fight, and now he has a bulletin his leg.

First Reporter: What shall I say about the peroxide blondes who made such a fuss at the ball game?
Second Reporter: Just say the bleachers went wild.

Question: What did one clover say to the other clover?
Answer: Take me to your weeder.

Hank: Why did Mr. Smith sleep under the oil tank last night?
Frank: Because he wanted to get up oily this morning.

Barry: What did the adding machine say to the cashier?
Gary: I don't know. What?
Barry: You can count on me.

Phil: Why do skunks argue?
Bill: I give up. Why?
Phil: Because they like to raise a stink.

First Ghost: I hear you've been haunting City Hall lately.
Second Ghost: That's right. I'm the nightmare.

Jan: Who was Snow White's brother?
Jon: I'll bite, who?
Jan: Egg White. Get the yolk?

IDIOT'S DELIGHT

here

A man walked up to a vending machine, put in a coin, and pressed the button labeled, "Coffee, double cream, sugar." No cup appeared. Then two nozzles went into action, one sending forth coffee, the other, cream. After the proper amounts had gone down the drain where the cup should have been, the machine turned off. "Now that's real automation," the man exclaimed. "This thing even drinks it for you."

Spud: Why is your dog running around in circles like that?
Dud: He's a watchdog and he's winding himself.

Smarty: I've just swallowed a great big worm.
Arty: Don't you think you should take something for it?
Smarty: No, I'll just let it starve.

Spud: Why does a Halloween witch ride a broom?
Dud: So she can sweep the sky.

One of the best marksmen in the FBI was passing through a small town. Everywhere he saw evidences of the most amazing shooting. On trees, on walls, and on fences there were numerous bull's-eyes with the bullet hole in dead center. The FBI man asked one of the townsmen if he could meet the person responsible for this wonderful marksmanship. The man turned out to be the village idiot.

"This is the best marksmanship I have ever seen," said the FBI man. "How in the world do you do it?"

"Nothing to it," said the idiot. "I shoot first and draw the circles afterward."

Dud: Did you hear about the man who sat down
    at dusk and waited to see where the sun went?
Spud: No, what happened?
Dud: It finally dawned on him!

Herbert was thoroughly fed up with his know-it-all
cousin from the city. At last he said, pointing, "I bet
you don't even know whether that's a Jersey cow." "Of
course I don't," was his reply. "I can't see its license."

Mr. Keen looked at Dopey Danny Dee and asked sympathetically, "Why are you limping this morning?"

Danny answered, "I strained myself coming out through the screen door."

Question: Why did Dopey Danny Dee make his dog sit near the fire?
Answer: Because he wanted to have a hot dog.

Spud: How did you break you leg?
Dud: I put a cigarette in an open manhole and stepped on it.

A man appeared at the police station one day and said he wanted to register a complaint.

"I've got three brothers," he explained. "We all live in one small apartment. One of my brothers has six cats. Another has eight dogs, and the third has a goat. The smell in there is just awful, and I'd like you to do something about it."

"Doesn't your apartment have any windows?" the policeman asked.

"Well, of course it has," the man answered.

"Then open them," the policeman suggested.

The man looked embarrassed and a little confused. "And lose all my pigeons?" he said.

Phil: Was it hot where you spent your summer vacation?

Will: Was it ever! There were no trees, so we took turns sitting in each other's shadows.

Burglar: The police are coming. Quick jump out the window!

Accomplice: But we're on the thirteenth floor.

Burglar: This is no time to be superstitious.

Sam: Did you hear the latest one about Danny?

Pam: No, what did he do now?

Sam: He says he won't buy a fall-out shelter. He's going to wait and buy a used one later.

Annie: What are you doing?

Danny: I'm writing a letter to a friend of mine.

Annie: Don't try to fool me. You can't write.

Danny: That doesn't make any difference. My friend can't read.

Dopey Danny Dee went into a store to buy a pillow case.

"What size?" asked the saleslady.

"I don't know," said Danny. "But I wear a size seven-and-a-quarter hat."

Three boys went into a general store at Brodlyville Corners. "I want a dime's worth of that hard candy on the top shelf," said the first boy.

Mr. Perkins went to the back of the store, got his stepladder, placed it under the shelf where the hard candy was, climbed up, filled a bag, came down, put the ladder away, and collected his dime.

"I want ten cents worth of that hard candy too," said the second boy.

Mr. Perkins went through the whole business again, but this time while he was at the top of the ladder, he asked the third boy if he wanted a dime's worth of candy too.

"No," replied the third boy.

Mr. Perkins put the ladder away again. Then he said to the third boy, "And what will you have?"

"A nickel's worth of hard candy," was the answer.

As a policeman was walking his beat along Park Avenue late one night, he saw a man on his hands and knees.

"Lose something?" the cop asked.

"Yes, I dropped a dollar on Tenth Street," the man answered.

"If you dropped a dollar on Tenth Street," said the cop, "why are you looking for it on Park Avenue?"

"Because, there's more light here," the man replied.

Little Larry: You told me if I rubbed grease on my chest, I'd grow tall like you, but it didn't work.
Tall Tim: What did you use?
Little Larry: Crisco.
Tall Tim: Stupid, that's shortening.

Dopey Danny Dee got a job nailing slats on poles to make fences. A friend of his came along and asked him why he was throwing half the nails away.

"Because the heads are on the wrong ends," Danny answered.

"You dumbbell," said his friend. "Those nails are for the other side of the fence."

Question: Why did Dopey Danny Dee jump off the Empire State Building?
Answer: Because he wanted to make a hit on Broadway.

When trudging home one day, Dopey Danny Dee met a friend. "Why don't you take a bus?" asked his friend.

"Because my mother will make me take it back," Danny replied.

Jim: Why does Danny always carry around a compass?
Slim: So he'll know whether he's coming or going.

Dopey Danny Dee heard a good joke and was going to take it home, but he decided that was carrying a joke too far.

Question: Why did Dopey Danny Dee take sugar and cream to the movies?
Answer: Because he heard they were having a new serial.

Les: I see you have an invitation to Jane's party.
Tess: Yes, but I can't go. It says 4 to 7, and I'm 10.

A high school boy took out of the library a book whose cover read *How to Hug,* only to discover it was Volume 7 of the Encyclopedia.

Question: Why did the dim-witted sergeant salute the refrigerator?
Answer: Because its name was "General Electric."

Question: Why did Dopey Danny Dee drive his truck
over the side of a cliff?

Answer: Because he wanted to try out his new air
brake.

Glen: Do you know what Danny was doing this morning?

Len: No, what?

Glen: He was standing in front of the mirror with
his eyes closed so he could see what he looks
like when he's asleep.

The kind old lady stopped Dopey Danny Dee on the street and said, "That's an unusual pair of socks you have on—one orange and one green."

"Yes," Danny answered. "And the funny thing is I've got another pair just like it at home."

Waldo: Guess what Danny did when he went to the movies?

Aldo: What?

Waldo: He went to see "The Desert" and asked for two tickets in the shade.

Aldo: That's nothing. Yesterday he stood in front of a mirror for a half hour trying to remember where he had seen himself before.

WORLD-WIDE WHIMSY

Question: How do you describe pedestrians in Los
    Angeles?
Answer: Los Angeles dodgers.

"Tell me," the missionary asked a cannibal, "do you think religion has made any progress here?"

"Yes," answered the native. "Now we eat only fishermen on Fridays."

An immigration officer asked a Chinese man his name.

"Sneeze," replied the man proudly.

"Is that Chinese?" asked the officer.

"No," said the man, "That's my American name."

"Then what is your Chinese name?" the officer inquired.

"Ah Choo!" was the reply.

Englishman: Your sky here looks much clearer than in London.
Bus Driver: Sure. We have more skyscrapers here.

Sally: What do you think about Red China?
Molly: It looks good with a white tablecloth.

Question: Why are the Isthmus of Suez and the first *U* in cucumber similar?
Answer: Because they are both between two seas.

Teacher: Which is farther away, South America or the moon?
Harvey: South America.
Teacher: South America? What makes you think that?
Harvey: We can see the moon, and we can't see South America.

A guide was showing a Texan Niagara Falls.

Guide: I'll bet you don't have anything like that in Texas.

Texan: Nope, I reckon we don't, but we got plumbers that could fix it.

Because of a dense fog, a Mississippi steamboat had to stop at the mouth of the river. A woman passenger demanded to know the cause of the delay. "Can't see up the river," the harassed captain replied. "Fog's too thick."

"But I can see the stars overhead," the woman said.

"Yes," the captain growled, "but unless the boilers explode, we're not going that way."

First Astronaut: Meet you on Jupiter tonight.

Second Astronaut: But how do I get there?

First Astronaut: When you get to the moon, turn left. You can't miss it.

Bert: Did you hear the Mexican weather report?

Gert: No, what is it?

Bert: Chili today and hot tamale.

Question: What is the difference between an Irishman frozen to death and a Scotsman at the North Pole?

Answer: One is killed with the cold; the other is cold with the kilt.

A man who had just bought a four-seater aircraft invited a friend to join him and his wife on its initial flight.

As soon as they were in the air, the owner, beaming, turned to his friend. "What I really enjoy about traveling this way," he said, "is the absolute sense of freedom it gives you. No worry about jaywalkers, no lights, no traffic jams. And best of all," he added with a wry smile, "no back-seat driving."

Suddenly his wife, who was sitting in the rear and peering out of the window, screamed, "Sam! For heaven's sake, watch out for those birds!"

Elderly Lady: A ticket for Cleveland, please.
Ticket Agent: Do you want to go by Buffalo?
Elderly Lady: No, better make it by train.

Bess: Gee, I'm sure glad I wasn't born in France.
Tess: Why do you say that?
Bess: Because I can't speak a word of French.

Mr. and Mrs. Jones were touring Russia. Their guide's name was Rudolph, and Mr. Jones and Rudolph argued all the time. As the couple was leaving Moscow, the husband said, "Look, it's snowing out."

The guide disagreed, "No, sir, it's raining out."

"I still think it's snowing," said Mr. Jones.

But his wife replied, "Rudolph the Red knows rain, dear."

An American tourist was in his bathing suit in the middle of the desert. An Arab rode by and blinked in amazement.

"I'm going swimming in the ocean," the tourist explained.

"But the ocean is eight hundred miles from here," said the Arab.

"Eight hundred miles!" said the tourist. "Boy, what a beach!"

Question: What do the Eskimos call their cows?
Answer: Eskimoos.

Eskimo Boy: What would you say if I told you I drove my dogsled five hundred miles over ice and snow just to tell you I love you?

Eskimo Girl: I'd say that's a lot of *mush!*

Worried Willy: Do ships this size sink very often?

Captain: No, sir. Never more than once.

Guide, on a safari in Africa: Quick, m'lord! Shoot that leopard right on the spot.

Lord Kinderling: Be specific, old man, which spot?

Teacher: Yes, Irving, Lapland is rather thinly populated.

Irving: How many Lapps to the mile, teacher?

While visiting London, a Texan was bragging about how big everything was in Texas. Annoyed by this, a London man put a two-hundred-pound turtle in the Texan's bed. When the Texan came out of his room yelling, "There's something in my bed!", the Londoner said, "I see you found one of our bedbugs!"

✓ Mrs. Inquisitive: Why were the Indians the first people in North America?

Mr. Know-It-All: Because they had reservations.

Alaskan: Our state is bigger than yours.

Texan: It won't be when it melts.

Mike: I know the capital of North Carolina.

Ike: Really?

Mike: No, Raleigh.

It was her first airplane trip, and Mrs. Smith was determined to be nonchalant about the whole thing. After reading a magazine for a while, she yawned and glanced out the window.

"My," she said to the man next to her, "people look just like ants from this height."

"Lady," replied her neighbor, "we haven't taken off yet. Those *are* ants."

The class was having a lesson in Geography, and the teacher asked, "Benny, where's the largest corn grown?"

"On Pop's little toe!" Benny replied.

Two Eskimos were passing an igloo. Said one to the other, "I'll bet he's awfully rich."

"Why do you say that?" asked the other Eskimo.

Answered the first, "His igloo's made of solid sherbet!"

Ned: What was a turtle doing on the New Jersey Turnpike?

Ted: About four miles an hour.

Harry: Why does the Statue of Liberty stand in New York Harbor?

Larry: Because she can't sit down.

Stu: Why is it that you can't starve in the Sahara Desert?

Sue: I think it's because of all the sand which is there.

Passenger: Is this my train?

Conductor: No sir, it belongs to the railroad company.

Passenger: Don't be funny. I mean can I take this train to New York?

Conductor: No, sir, it's much too heavy.

An American was visiting in Australia. "Don't you think that tower is beautiful?" asked his Australian guide.

"Well, now," said the American, "we've got towers as big as that or bigger at home."

"What about this road?" asked the Aussie. "Have you ever seen any like it before?"

"Why sure," said the visitor. "We've got lots of roads longer and wider than that."

They continued walking until they came to a field. Suddenly they saw a kangaroo hop by. "Well," said the American, "one thing I'll have to admit. Your grasshoppers are a little larger than ours at home."

Teacher: Keith, can you name the fiftieth state?

Keith: Huh? Why . . . uh . . .

Teacher: Correct.

A hiker traveling the mountains of Arizona came upon an Indian sending smoke signals. When asked how big a fire he usually built, the Indian replied, "It all depends on whether it's a local or a long-distance call."

Jim: Where do you have the longest view in the world?
Tim: By a roadside lined with telephone poles. Because there you can see from pole to pole.

Bea: People must grow awfully large in England.
Lee: Why?
Bea: I read in *The London Times* about a woman who lost five hundred pounds.

Question: Why do Eskimos weep so much?
Answer: Each Eskimo must have his daily blubber.

Gus: What did Tennessee?
Gert: The same as Arkansas.

Oliver: Dad, have you ever been to Egypt?

Dad: No, why?

Oliver: Well, where did you get Mummy?

Stu: Ever since Missouri built that giant metallic arch on the St. Louis riverfront, Illinois has been jealous. Now Illinois has thought up something to deflate Missouri.

Sue: What are they going to do?

Stu: Across the river from the arch, on its own side, Illinois is going to build a huge man with a croquet mallet.

A lady tourist, admiring an Indian's necklace, asked him, "What are you wearing around your neck?"

"Alligator teeth," the Indian answered.

After recovering from her initial shock, the lady said, "Well, I suppose that they hold the same meaning for you as pearls do for us."

"Not quite," he answered. "Anybody can open an oyster."

A ship's captain was telling of his adventures at sea. "In a thick ocean fog I saw a light in the distance. Slowly it became clearer and clearer, and finally I could make it out. It was the end of my cigarette."

The Russians don't need missiles to destroy us. All they have to do is poison the glue on the backs of trading stamps.

Teacher: Do you know why the flag of the U.S.A.
has stars and that of Japan has the sun?
Student: That's easy. Because it's daytime in Japan
when it's night in the U.S.A.

An Eskimo mother was sitting in her igloo reading
rhymes to her young daughter. "Little Jack Horner sat
in a corner . . ."

"Mother," interrupted the youngster, "what's a corner?"

Billy: Where was Solomon's temple?
Silly: On the side of his head.

Sam: What do they call the Golden Gate Bridge at
5 P.M.?
Pam: The car-spangled spanner.

Teacher: John, in what part of the world are people
most ignorant?
John: New York City.
Teacher: Nonsense! What makes you say that?
John: My geography book says that's where the popula-
tion is most dense.

Benny: Have you ever caught the German measles?
Penny: No, I haven't even been to Germany.

Donald: Why are telephone rates high in Iran?
Ronald: Because everyone there speaks Persian to Persian.

Jet planes can travel faster than sound. I wonder how soon it will be before they have one that will travel faster than rumor.

Ella: I just flew in from Europe.
Della: I'll bet your arms are tired.

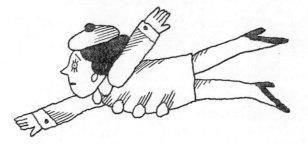

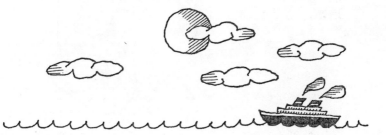

ANIMAL ANTICS

First Dog: My name is Spot. What's yours?
Second Dog: I'm not sure, but I think it's Down Boy.

A little boy sat before the fireplace stroking his new kitten. When it suddenly began to purr loudly, the boy jerked it roughly away from the hearth. "Can't you treat your new pet more gently?" his mother asked. "But, Mom," the boy retorted, "I had to move it quickly . . . didn't you hear it start to boil?"

Harry: What kind of dog is that?
Barry: He's a police dog.
Harry: He sure doesn't look like one to me.
Barry: Of course not. He's in the Secret Service.

Question: What did the baby porcupine say when he backed into a cactus?
Answer: Is that you, Ma?

Question: On which side does a chicken have the most feathers?
Answer: Outside!

Question: What do hippopotamuses have that no other animals have?
Answer: Little hippopotamuses.

Saul: If your dog were eating your book, what would you do?
Paul: I would take the words right out of his mouth.

Question: What gallops down the road on its head?
Answer: A horseshoe nail.

Question: What would you get if you crossed a flea
  with a rabbit?
Answer: A bug's bunny.

Question: What bird is the most impudent?
Answer: A mockingbird.

A baby sardine saw a submarine for the first time.
"What is that?" he asked his mother in a fearful voice.
"Don't be scared," she replied. "It's just a can of
people."

William announced that he was going to feed his sheep
ironized yeast. His father asked him why. "So I'll be able
to get steel wool," said the boy.

Fran: Does the giraffe get a sore throat if he gets his
  feet wet?
Ann: I suppose so, but not until the next week.

Bob: Did I ever tell you about the time I came face to
  face with a lion?
Rob: No, what happened?
Bob: There I stood without a gun. The lion growled
  ferociously, and crept closer and closer. . . .
Rob: Gee! What did you do?
Bob: I moved on to the next cage.

Question: Why do giraffes have such small appetites?
Answer: Because with them a little goes a long way.

A magician had a pet parrot that he used in his show. The parrot had seen the act so many times that he was very bored. One day the magician got a job entertaining the passengers on an ocean liner. He went through his usual routine of pulling rabbits out of a hat and making them vanish and tossing glasses into the air, where they disappeared. All the while the parrot looked on, growing increasingly restless.

Suddenly one night the boilers in the engine room of the ship exploded. The ship sank and the magician and the parrot found themselves sitting at opposite ends of a life raft. They sat and stared at each other saying nothing for quite a while, but curiosity finally overcame the parrot and he asked, "Okay, wiseguy, what did you do with it?"

Two large turtles and a small one went into an ice cream parlor and ordered three sundaes. While they were waiting for the soda jerk to fill their orders, they noticed it had started to rain.

"We're going to need our umbrella," said one big turtle, and the other big one agreed. The two of them decided that the little turtle should run home and get the umbrella. But the little turtle didn't want to go because he was afraid the two big turtles would eat his sundae. However, they promised not to, and finally the little turtle started off.

A week went by, then two weeks. At the end of the third week one of the big turtles turned to the other and said, "Aw, come on, let's eat his sundae."

"Okay, let's," agreed his companion.

"If you do, I won't go for that umbrella," cried the little turtle, sticking his head out from under the counter at the other end of the shop.

Mack: Why did the parrot carry an umbrella?
Jack: I don't know, why did he?
Mack: So he could be Polly-unsaturated!

Dick: A snake just snapped at me.
Nick: Don't be silly. Snakes don't snap.
Dick: This one did. It was a garter snake.

Question: What animal eats the least?
Answer: The moth. It just eats holes.

Al: I've got a smarter cat than you have.
Pal: How do you know?
Al: It eats cheese and then waits at a mousehole with baited breath.

Question: How can you find a rabbit that is lost in the woods?
Answer: Make a noise like a carrot.

Question: What should you do if you wake up in the middle of the night and hear a mouse squeaking?
Answer: Oil it.

Boy Mosquito: What are you making such a fuss about?
Girl Mosquito: Yippee! I just passed the screen test!

A man was out strolling in the woods when he came across a very strange-looking animal. It seemed to be half rabbit and half chipmunk. He dashed home, picked up the phone, called a number, then waited and waited. Growing impatient at last, he signaled the operator and demanded, "Why can't you get me the zoo?"

"Sorry, sir," said the operator. "Lion's busy."

Ron: Why does a monkey scratch himself?
Don: I don't know. Why?
Ron: Because he's the only one who knows where it itches.

Sandy: Isn't it wonderful how little chicks get out of their shells?

Mandy: It's more wonderful how they get in.

Question: What did the choking frog say to the other frog?

Answer: I must have a person in my throat.

Question: Why is an ice-cream cone like a horse?

Answer: The more you lick it, the faster it goes.

"Oh, Mother," cried the little boy when he saw a snake for the first time, "come here quick. Here's a tail wagging without any dog!"

Mrs. Harris: Willy, have you given the goldfish fresh water today?

Willy: No. They haven't finished what I gave them yesterday.

Kangaroo (complaining to a psychiatrist): I don't know what's the matter with me. I just don't feel jumpy anymore.

Question: Where does a sheep get his hair cut?
Answer: At a baa-baa shop.

Question: Why couldn't the pony talk?
Answer: He was a little horse.

Question: Why is it hard to talk with a goat around?
Answer: Because he always butts in.

Question: What's the best way to catch a squirrel?
Answer: Climb a tree and act like a nut.

A small boy who was told to go to the henhouse to collect some eggs corrected his father's choice of words. His father responded, "I don't care if she's sittin' or settin', but when she starts cacklin', I want to know whether she's layin' or lyin'."

First Sheep: Baa-a-a.
Second Sheep: Moo!
First Sheep: What do you mean "moo?"
Second Sheep: I'm learning a foreign language.

Mary: What did the beaver say to the tree?
Gary: I don't know. What?
Mary: It was nice gnawing you.

Question: Why was the horse called a hot-head?
Answer: Because he had a blaze on his forehead.

Question: What is a good way to keep a dog off the
    street?
Answer: Put him in a barking lot.

Jim: Is it really bad luck to have a black cat follow
    you?
Tim: Well, it depends on whether you're a man or a
    mouse.

Tina: A girl camel with two humps married a boy
    camel with one hump. They had a baby camel
    with no humps. Do you know what they called
    him?
Lena: No, what?
Tina: Humphrey.

Jed: Did you hear about the rabbit with the lisp who
    went to the dentist to get his tooth extracted?
Red: No.
Jed: The dentist asked him if he wanted gas, and the
    rabbit answered, "No, I'm an ether bunny."

Farmer: How do you treat a pig with a sore throat?
Veterinarian: Apply oinkment.

Question: What did one kangaroo say to another kangaroo during a snowstorm?

Answer: I wish it would stop snowing—I hate to have my kid cooped up like this.

Mrs. Dogood went to the ASPCA to get a dog as a present for her son. "Are you sure this one will make a good pet?" she asked. "Certainly, ma'am," said the ASPCA man. "He's very gentle. He'll eat anything, and he's especially fond of children."

Harry: What would you do if a friend told you he killed a thirteen-foot lion in Africa?

Herb: Tell him that is some "lyin."

Peg: Did you hear the story about the peacock?
Meg: No, I didn't.
Peg: It's a beautiful tale.

A lady went to an auction and found something she wanted very badly. It was a parrot, and she decided to bid for it. The bids went higher and higher, but finally she got the bird for $49.54. Then it suddenly occurred to her that she hadn't found out the most important thing about the bird. "Does it talk?" she asked the auctioneer. The auctioneer smiled. "Who do you think was bidding against you all the time?" he replied.

The teller selling three-dollar tickets at the race track was astonished to see a horse step up to the window and ask to bet on himself.

"What's the matter?" snorted the horse. "Are you surprised that I can talk?"

"Not at all," said the man. "I'm surprised that you think you can win!"

Since female chicks sell more readily than male, Western chicken breeders often hire certain Orientals who have a secret way of telling the male chick from the female. One rumor has it that the Orientals operate this way: they throw corn to a chick; if he eats it, the chick is a male. If she eats it, the chick is female.

Question: What did the hen say when she saw a plate
of scrambled eggs?
Answer: What a crazy bunch of mixed-up kids!

Sam: How is a skunk different from a rabbit?
Pam: I don't know. How?
Sam: The skunk uses a cheaper deodorant.

Question: What is a bull called when he's sleeping?
Answer: A bulldozer.

Belle: My dog swallowed a flashlight yesterday.
Mel: Is he sick?
Belle: No, he spit it out last night, and now he's de-
lighted.

A deer and an antelope were out on the prairie. The
antelope suddenly stopped and cocked his head. The
deer asked, "What's wrong?" The antelope answered,
"I thought I just heard a discouraging word."

Little Boy Blue: Baa, baa, black sheep, have you any
wool?
Black Sheep: What do you think this is, wiseguy, ny-
lon?

Mrs. Owl: I'm worried about baby owl.
Mr. Owl: Why?
Mrs. Owl: He doesn't give a hoot about anything.

Question: Why is a porcupine so nervous?
Answer: Because he is on pins and needles.

Question: What do you call a cat who drinks lemonade?
Answer: A sourpuss.

Arty: If you were surrounded by twenty lions, fifteen tigers, and ten leopards, how would you get away from them?
Smarty: Stop the merry-go-round and get off!

Nat: What kind of animals can jump higher than a house?
Pat: I have no idea.
Nat: Silly! All kinds of animals. Houses can't jump.

Polly: Are bees very good at arguments?
Molly: I don't know. Are they?
Polly: Well, they always carry their point.

Al: Why did the city rat gnaw a hole in the carpet?
Sal: Tell me. Why?
Al: Because he wanted to see the floor show.

Question: Why has a horse got six legs?
Answer: Because he has forelegs in front and two legs behind.

Question: What animal is a cannibal?
Answer: A cow. It eats its fodder.

Once there were three skunks, a mama skunk, and two little skunks named Albert and Elbert. One day Elbert asked his mother, "Can I have a chemistry set?"

"No," said his mother, "you may smell up the house!"

Question: What is unusual about the way a horse eats?
Answer: He eats best when he hasn't a bit in his mouth.

Question: What's black and white and red all over?
Answer: A sunburned zebra.

Chipmunk: Say, Beaver, they tell me you can cut down any size tree.
Beaver: Well, I've never been stumped yet.

Billy took his dog with him to the movie of "Winnie-The-Pooh." The dog sat in the seat next to him. When the usher came along and noticed the dog, he was about to throw it out. But then he saw that the animal seemed to be paying close attention to the movie so he let him stay. After the show the usher went over to the boy. "It certainly surprised me to see your dog enjoying the film," he said.

"It surprised me, too," the boy replied. "He didn't like the book at all."

Question: How does an octopus go into battle?
Answer: Well armed.

Frank: Tom was put in jail for stealing a pig!
Hank: How could they prove he did it?
Frank: The pig squealed.

Question: What is the best year for a kangaroo?
Answer: Leap year.

Sue: Did you hear about the horse who ate an electric
     wire instead of hay?
Lew: No, what happened?
Sue: He went haywire.

Question: Why shouldn't you cry when a cow falls on
   the ice?
Answer: Because it is no use crying over spilled milk.

Barry: Why are four-legged animals poor dancers?
Larry: I don't know. Why?
Barry: Because they have two left feet.

Question: Why can't a pig get sick?
Answer: Because it has to be killed before it can be
   cured.

Question: If you fed a cow money, what would you
   get?
Answer: Rich milk.

Question: What is worse than a giraffe with a sore
   throat?
Answer: An elephant with a bloody nose.

THE SCIENCE SCENE

A group of scientists had just completed an important experiment.

First Scientist: Men, we have finally discovered an acid that will eat up everything.

Second Scientist: That's just fine, but I have one question. What are we going to keep it in?

Jim: Oh, darn! I got 100 in science today and still didn't pass.

Father (horrified): Why not, for goodness' sake?

Jim: The answer was 200.

Don: Do you know what would happen if you swallowed uranium?

Ron: Nope.

Don: You'd get a-tomic ache.

Denny: Isn't it amazing! Just think. Light travels at the rate of 186,000 miles a second!

Benny: That's not so great. It's downhill all the way.

Science Teacher: Name a liquid that can't freeze.

Student: Hot water.

Question: Why did the germ cross the microscope?

Answer: To get to the other slide.

Science Teacher: This gas is deadly poison. What steps would you take if it escaped?

Billy (quickly): Large ones, sir.

Jane: Can you tell me what moves slower than a snail, but flies faster than a bird?

John: No. What?

Jane: Molecules in an airplane.

Science Teacher: What do bees do with their honey?

Student: They cell it.

One day a nervous woman was introduced to a prominent astronomer.

"Do you think it's possible for nuclear weapons to destroy the earth?" she asked.

"Suppose they do," replied the great scientist casually. "After all, it isn't as if the earth was a major planet."

Will: How can you carry water in a sieve?
Jill: I don't know. How?
Will: Freeze it.

Chemistry Teacher: What does HNO₃ stand for?
Stalling Student: HNO₃ . . . let's see . . . Hm-m . . .
    It's on the tip of my tongue.
Chemistry Teacher: Well, spit it out boy! It's nitric
    acid!

Mack: Did you hear about the two blood cells?
Jack: No, what happened?
Mack: They loved in vein.

Teacher: Sally, can you name the four seasons?
Sally: Salt, pepper, mustard, and vinegar.

Hip: It's a good thing adults split atoms.
Chip: Why?
Hip: Well, if we did it, they'd make us put them back
    together.

Question: What did the protoplasm say to the amoeba?
Answer: Don't bacilli.

Letter to the Weather Bureau:

I thought you'd be interested in knowing that I shoveled three feet of "partly cloudy" from my front porch this morning.

First Scientist: I've just made a wonderful discovery— how to make wool out of milk.

Second Scientist: That's great. But it must make the cow feel a little sheepish.

An atomic scientist went away on vacation. In his absence, a sign was hung on his office door reading: GONE FISSION!

Ned: Do you know three letters that stand for hard water?

Ed: No, I don't.

Ned: *I-C-E.*

One day two guinea pigs were conversing with each other through the bars of their laboratory cages. One, looking up, noticed a scientist advancing upon his cage and carrying a huge hypodermic needle. "Oh, no!" groaned the pig. "Here comes that man with his needle again!" Then, aside to his friend, he bitterly confided, "You know, he makes me sick!"

Teacher: Sid, what is the highest form of animal life?

Sid: I think it's the giraffe.

"Stan," said the chemistry teacher, "give me the formula for water."

"Yes, sir," said Stan, *"H,I,J,K,L,M,N,O."*

"Just a minute," said the teacher. "You're not in kindergarten, you know."

"No, sir," said Stan, "but you said yesterday it was *H* to *O.*"

Father: Roger, how come all of a sudden you're such a nature lover?

Roger: Since the Beatles, the Rolling Stones, the Byrds, and the Animals.

Chemistry Teacher: What is HIOAg?
Bright Pupil: Hi-O Silver!

Question: What do the stars do when they get hungry?
Answer: They take a bite of the Milky Way.

Voice on Phone: Hello, is this the Weather Bureau?
Weatherman: Yes, it is.
Voice on Phone: How're chances for a shower tonight?
Weatherman: It's okay with me, sir—take one if you
    need it!

Sam: What kind of bulbs should you never water?
Pam: Wow, that's a tough one! What kind?
Sam: Light bulbs.

Teacher: Do you know what a satellite is?
Student: Sure, it's what you put on your horse if you're going to ride him after dark.

Question: What causes a flood?
Answer: A river that gets too big for its bridges!

Rob: Why is *B* hot?
Bob: I have no idea.
Rob: Because it makes oil boil.

Question: How many balls of string would it take to reach the moon?
Answer: Only one, if it were long enough.

Question: Why haven't they sent the three-man rocket to the moon yet?
Answer: Because they can't decide what movie to show.

Professor: Give the most important fact about nitrates.
Pupil: They're cheaper than day rates.

Ron: I hear that the moon is going broke.
Don: Where did you hear that?
Ron: Well, it said in the paper that the moon was down to its last quarter.

Prospective Tenant: Didn't you say this apartment was occupied by an experimental scientist? I guess those spots on the wall are from his experiments?
Landlord: No, those spots are the scientist!

Question: What did one atom say to the other atom?
Answer: Let's split up and charge the town!

An apple dropping on his head
  set Newton thinking, but—
The story might have been different
  had it been a coconut.

Did you hear about the political-minded ion who, hearing there was going to be an electron, went to the poles and volted?

Bill: How is an earthquake like a malted milk?
Phil: I don't know. How?
Bill: They are both big shakes.

Lenny: Which travels slower—heat or cold?
Denny: I don't know. Which?
Lenny: Cold—you can catch cold easily.

Question: What kind of sentence would you get if you
broke the law of gravity?
Answer: A suspended one.

Science Teacher: Sue, can you give me an example of
how water attracts electricity?
Sue: Yes, sir! Every time I get into the bathtub the
phone rings.

Teacher: Now, we all know that when certain sub-
stances are heated, they expand and when they
are cooled, they contract. Richard, can you give me
an example of this?
Richard: Well, in the winter the days are short and in
the summer the days are long.

RIDDLE DE DIDDLE

Question: What goes up into the air white and comes
down yellow and white?
Answer: An egg.

Question: What time is it when you sit on a tack?
Answer: Spring time.

Question: What do you call a frightened skindiver?
Answer: Chicken of the sea.

Question: What is the difference between a cat and a
    comma?
Answer: A cat has claws at the end of its paws, and
    a comma has a pause at the end of its clause.

Question: What's the longest piece of furniture in the
    world?
Answer: The multiplication table.

Question: What kind of coat can be put on only when
    wet?
Answer: A coat of paint.

Question: Why do cows wear cowbells?
Answer: Because their horns don't work.

Question: What tree does everyone carry in his hand?
Answer: The palm.

Question: How do you tell a story?
Answer: It's where the elevator stops.

Question: What do you get when you cross a goat and
    an owl?
Answer: A hootenanny.

Question: What has nothing left but *nose* when it loses an eye?
Answer: *Noise.*

Question: How can a leopard change his spots?
Answer: By moving.

Question: What can go up a chimney down, but can't come down a chimney up?
Answer: An umbrella.

Question: What turns without moving?
Answer: Milk. It can turn sour.

Question: When does a boat show affection?
Answer: When it hugs the shore.

Question: When you lose something, why do you always
    find it in the last place you look?
Answer: Because you stop looking as soon as you find
    it.

Question: Why does a baby pig eat so much?
Answer: To make a hog of himself.

Question: Where does a jellyfish get its jelly?
Answer: From ocean currents.

Question: What do you get when you cross a monster
    with a drip-dry suit?
Answer: A wash-and-wear wolf.

Question: Why is a coward like a leaky faucet?
Answer: They both run.

Question: What did one eye say to the other eye?
Answer: There's something in between that smells.

Question: What gives us milk and has one horn?
Answer: A milk truck.

Question: If a farmer raises wheat in dry weather, what
    does he raise in wet weather?
Answer: An umbrella.

Question: What did the razor blade say to the razor?
Answer: Schick 'em up!

Question: What four letters could end a game of hide and seek.
Answer: *O-I-C-U*.

Question: What ring is best for a telephone?
Answer: Answer-ring.

Question: Why is your hand similar to a hardware store?
Answer: Because it has nails.

Question: What's higher than a house and seems smaller than a mouse?
Answer: A star.

Question: What day of the year is a command to go forward?
Answer: March 4th.

Question: When does a sea seem to be friendly?
Answer: When it waves.

Question: What is long and gray and slippery and whistles "Dixie" backwards?
Answer: Robert E. Eel.

Question: Why is a crossword puzzle like a quarrel?
Answer: Because one word leads to another.

Question: What did the envelope say when the boy licked it?

Answer: It just shut up and said nothing.

Question: Why does lightning shock people?

Answer: Because it doesn't know how to conduct itself.

Question: What is the best way to hide a bear?

Answer: Skin him.

Question: Why did the little boy sleep on the chandelier?

Answer: Because he was a light sleeper.

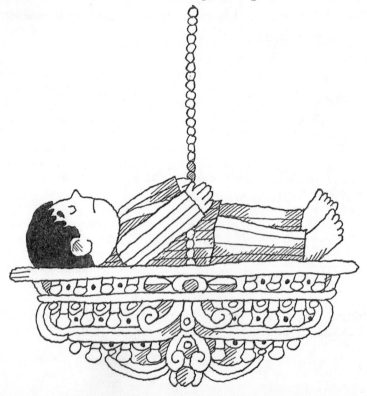

Question: Why are rivers always rich?
Answer: Because they have two banks.

Question: What keys do not open locks?
Answer: A don-key, a mon-key, and a tur-key.

Question: What soap is the hardest?
Answer: Cast-steel (castile).

Question: What has four wheels and flies?
Answer: A garbage truck.

Question: Why is a watermelon filled with water?
Answer: Because it is planted in the spring.

Question: How does a witch tell time?
Answer: With a witch watch!

Question: Why is the letter *E* like London?
Answer: Because it is the capital in England.

Question: What is sold by the yard and worn by the
foot?
Answer: A carpet.

Question: When does a bed change size?
Answer: At night, when two feet are added to it.

Question: Why is an icy sidewalk like music?
Answer: If you don't see sharp, you'll be flat.

Question: Why were the soldiers tired on April Fool's Day?

Answer: Because they had just had a March of thirty-one days.

Question: What did the painter say to the wall?

Answer: One more crack like that, and I'll plaster you.

Question: What sort of wind do we look for after Lent?

Answer: An Easterly wind.

Question: If all the people in the U.S. owned pink cars, what would the country be called?

Answer: A pink carnation.

Question: Why did the woman go to the store and buy twelve loaves of bread?

Answer: Because she saw a sign saying RAISIN' BREAD TOMORROW.

Question: What stays hot in the refrigerator?

Answer: Mustard.

Question: At what time of day was Adam created?

Answer: A little before Eve.

Question: Why are pins always getting lost?

Answer: Because they are pointed in one direction, and headed in another.

Question: Why is a blotter like a lazy dog?
Answer: Because a blotter is an ink-lined plane; an inclined plane is a slope up; and a slow pup is a lazy dog.

Question: How do you make anti-freeze?
Answer: Steal her blanket.

Question: What grows larger the more you take away?
Answer: A hole.

Question: Who was the first skindiver?
Answer: A mosquito.

Question: What did one ear say to the other?
Answer: I didn't know we lived on the same block.

Question: What do you call a monkey that sells potato chips?
Answer: A chip monk.

Question: Why do people laugh up their sleeves?
Answer: Because that's where their funny bones are.

Question: What is the tallest building in the world?
Answer: The library, because it has the most stories.

Question: What are two germs living together called?
Answer: Cellmates.

Question: What bird can lift the heaviest weights?
Answer: The crane.

Question: How does one dinosaur tell another to hurry up?
Answer: Pronto, Saurus!

Question: Where does a witch keep her spaceship?
Answer: In the broom closet.

Question: What's black and yellow and goes, "Zub-zub-zub?"
Answer: A bee flying backwards.

Question: What has a big mouth but can't talk?
Answer: A jar.

Question: What has a mouth but can't speak and a bed that can't be slept in?
Answer: A river.

Question: Why doesn't the ocean overflow the land?
Answer: Because it is tide.

Question: How many dead people are there in a cemetery?
Answer: All of them.

Question: What is the last word in airplanes?
Answer: Jump.

Question: Why is Sunday the strongest day?
Answer: Because all the others are weekdays.

Question: What is a forum?
Answer: Two-um plus two-um.

Question: What two animals go with you everywhere?
Answer: Your calves.

Question: What's a cocoon?
Answer: A wound-up caterpillar.

Question: What has many leaves but no stem?
Answer: A book.

Question: When does roast beef cost the most?
Answer: When it is rarest.

Question: How is a doormat related to a doorstep?
Answer: It's a stepfather (farther).

Question: What starts with *E*, ends with *E*, and has one
    letter in it?
Answer: An envelope.

Question: What's the difference between an unhappy
    boy and grass?
Answer: One is sad; the other is sod.

Question: What time spelled backward and forward is
    the same?
Answer: Noon.

Question: Why is a large coat like a banana peel?
Answer: Both are easy to slip on.

Question: Where were the first doughnuts fried?
Answer: In Greece.

Question: When is a spanking like a hat?
Answer: When it is felt.

Question: What sort of bed is a three-season bed?
Answer: One without a spring.

Question: When is the ocean like a piece of string?
Answer: When a ship makes knots in it.

Question: Why is a half moon heavier than a full
    moon?
Answer: Because a full moon is lighter.

Question: What Roman numeral can climb a wall?
Answer: IV.

Question: When does it rain money?
Answer: Whenever there's some change in the weather.

Question: What is the difference between a funny
    Dutchman and a hollow tube?
Answer: One is a silly Hollander. The other is a hollow
    cylinder.

Question: When do ghosts have the most fun?
Answer: Whenever they're in high spirits.

Question: What is the spooks' defense system called?
Answer: The Ghost Guard.

Question: Why did the man throw his pants out the
    window?
Answer: Because he heard the newsboy crying, "Free
    Press."

Question: What puts the white lines on the ocean?
Answer: An ocean liner.

Question: What did the tie say to the hat?
Answer: You go on ahead, I'll just hang around.

Question: What did one candle ask the other candle?
Answer: Are you going out tonight?

Question: Why is the sea restless at night?
Answer: You would be too, if you had rocks in your
    bed.

Question: What is a HIbVE?
Answer: A small bee in a big hive.

Question: What is fast when it doesn't run, and is not
    fast when it does run?
Answer: Madras.

Question: When is a river like the letter *T?*
Answer: When it must be crossed.

Question: What goes further the slower it goes?
Answer: Your money.

SPORT SHORTS

Rick: Why does a golfer wear two pairs of pants?
Dick: I have no idea.
Rick: In case he makes a hole in one.

Question: What do a baseball team and a dish set have
    in common?
Answer: They both have pitchers.

Bob: Here's one for you. The Marines and Navy were
    playing basketball. All the Marines fouled out.
    Who would they put in?
Rob: I don't know.
Bob: The sub-marines.

Red: Did you mark that place where the fishing was
    good?
Ted: Yes, I put an *X* on the side of the boat.
Red: That was stupid. What if we should take out an-
    other boat next time?

This was the first time he had taken his girl fishing.
After a few minutes with their lines in the water, she
asked, "What did that yellow-and-white thing on my
line cost?"
    "The bobber? Oh, about a quarter, why?"
    "Well, I owe you a quarter. Mine just sank."

Instructor at a Riding Academy: What kind of saddle
    would you prefer—one with a horn, or one with-
    out?
Novice: Without, I guess. There doesn't seem to be
    much traffic around here.

Pam: Do you know how fishermen make their nets?
Sam: It's simple, Pam. They just take a handful of
    holes, sew them together, and there you are.

Wally: Do you know how to play baseball?
Sally: Sure I do.
Wally: Then tell me how you hold a bat?
Sally: By the wings of course.

Don: What race always starts with a tie?
Ron: I don't know.
Don: A three-legged race.

Question: Why was Adam a famous runner?
Answer: Because in the human race he was first.

Policeman: I'm going to have to arrest you for going swimming in this pond.

Coy Miss: But officer, you could have told me before I changed into my bathing suit.

Policeman: There isn't any law against that, miss.

The new neighbor was calling on Mrs. Jones. "I hear your son is a fine football player," she said. "What position does he play?"

"Oh," Mrs. Jones answered, "I think he's one of the drawbacks."

Two Indians were on a riverbank watching a motorboat pulling a man on water skis. After a few minutes of observation, one of the natives asked, "What makes big canoe go so fast?" The other answered, "Man on string chase-um."

Clancy: Say, did you know that I've got a baseball dog?

Nancy: What is a baseball dog?

Clancy: Well, he wears a muzzle, catches flies, chases fowls, and beats it for home when he sees the catcher coming.

Coach: Ronny, I'll let you be end, guard, and tackle in the Thanksgiving Day game.

Ronny: How can I do that?

Coach: You just sit at the end of the bench, guard the water bucket, and tackle anybody that gets close to it.

Dick: Why has Mickey Mantle so much money?
Nick: I don't know. Why?
Dick: Well, a good batter usually makes good dough.

John had been fishing all day with no luck. On his way home, he entered a fish market and asked the clerk, "Mister, just stand there and throw me several of your biggest bass." The clerk was puzzled. "Throw them? What's the idea?" John replied, "I may be a bad fisherman, but I'm not a liar. I want to be able to tell my family that I caught them."

Question: Why was Cinderella thrown off the baseball
team?
Answer: Because she ran away from the ball.

Olly: What would you get if Mickey Mantle married
Betty Crocker?
Polly: I don't know. What?
Olly: A better batter.

Bob: I went riding this afternoon.
Rob: Horseback?
Bob: Oh, yes. He got back two hours before I did.

Two boys were on their first camping trip. Mosquitoes
started to bother them so they got under the blanket
and hid. Later, one boy peeked out and saw several
fireflies. He remarked, "We might as well give up, Tony.
These things are out searching for us with lights now."

Mandy: I went horseback riding for the first time today.
Randy: Did you like it?
Mandy: I never knew anything filled with hay could
feel so hard.

Stan: Do you know why a baseball stadium is always
cool?
Dan: No, why?
Stan: Because it has fans in every seat.

Len: Gee, I'm depressed.

Glen: But why should you be if your girl said she'd
be faithful to the end?

Len: Because I'm the halfback!

John: Why did the quarterback tie a rope to the football during a game?

Don: I don't know. Why?

John: Because he wanted to tie up the score.

Mother: Remember not to go into the water right after lunch. It's dangerous to swim on a full stomach.
Smarty: That's all right. I'll swim on my back.

Question: Why is tennis such a noisy game?
Answer: Because each player raises a racket.

Question: What has eighteen legs and catches flies?
Answer: A baseball team.

Stranger: Catch any fish?
Fisherman: Did I! I took thirty out of this stream this morning.
Stranger: Do you know who I am? I'm the game warden.
Fisherman: Do you know who I am? I'm the biggest liar in the country.

Question: What is the biggest jewel in the world?
Answer: A baseball diamond.

There were three men in a boat halfway across a lake. The first man suddenly said, "I forgot my lunch," got out of the boat and walked to shore on top of the water. Later, the second man said, "I forgot my fishing tackle," and also walked across the water to shore. By this time, the third man thought to himself, "They're not going to outsmart me. I forgot my bait can," and he started to walk across the water, but he sank. The first man said to the second, "Maybe we should have told him where the rocks were?"

The teacher asked the class to write a composition on baseball. One minute later, little Allen turned in his paper. It read: "Game called on account of rain."

It was hunting season when a state trooper walked up to a man and his son, and said, "That's a nice buck you have on the top of your car." The surprised man couldn't say anything, so his son answered for him, "That's nothing. You should see the one we have in the trunk."

A scout leader on a camping trip was sick and tired of answering questions. Finally he made a rule: anyone who asked a question that he himself couldn't answer would have to wash everybody else's mess kit after supper.

This didn't stop Danny, who asked more questions than anyone else. Immediately he said, "When a chipmunk digs its hole, why doesn't it leave a heap of dirt around the entrance?"

"Answer it yourself!" the others shouted gleefully.

"A chipmunk starts digging its hole at the other end," Danny explained.

The scoutmaster looked at him scornfully. "How could it get to the other end to start digging?" he said.

"You made the rule," Danny answered. "Start washing."

Question: What is it that travels about and wears out shoes, but has no shoes to wear?
Answer: A football.

Jim: Why are you taking your math lesson to gym?
Tim: Because I have some fractions to reduce!

Question: How does modern baseball resemble ancient
    Greek literature?
Answer: They both have homers.

> I threw a pass into the air.
> It fell to earth, I know not where.
> And that is why I sit and dream
> Upon the bench with the third-string team.

Question: When a librarian goes fishing, what does she
    use for bait?
Answer: Bookworms.

Ed: Did you hear about the absent-minded professor
    who fell overboard and drowned?
Fred: No, what happened?
Ed: He forgot he couldn't swim.

May: Did you see those baseball stockings Marjorie wore today?

Fay: Baseball stockings?

May: Of course. They had three big runs in them, didn't they?

Little Johnny, smirkingly, to new neighbor: "I'll be glad to have you over to my swimming pool anytime for a drowning lesson."

Joe: Why didn't they play cards on Noah's Ark?

Moe: I don't know. Tell me.

Joe: Because Noah sat on the deck.

Sam: I went out for the football team.

Pam: What happened?

Sam: Well, I thought I made it. The first day at practice the coach looked at me and said, "This is the end!"

Aldo: When was tennis mentioned in the Bible?

Waldo: I don't know, when?

Aldo: When Joseph served in Pharaoh's court.

Game Warden: You can't catch fish without a permit.

Fisherman: I'm doing fine with just a worm, thank you.

FEAST OR FAMINE

Question: What did the fat man say when he sat down
to eat his dinner?
Answer: I'm afraid this food is all going to waist.

Jed: May I have a hamburger?
Ted: With pleasure.
Jed: No, with pickles and onions.

One day while driving in a thunderstorm, a man got a flat tire outside a monastery. A monk came out and invited him inside to have dinner and spend the night. The motorist accepted. That night he had a wonderful dinner of fish and chips. He decided to compliment the chef. Entering the kitchen, he asked the cook, "Are you the fish friar?" "No," the man replied, "I'm the chip monk."

Waiter: How did you find your steak, sir?
Diner: Just by accident. I moved the baked potato and
        there it was.

Mr. Mutton: Where do you usually dine?
Mr. Glutton: Oh, I always eat in restaurants where they
        serve soup to nuts.

Diner: I can't eat this food. Call the manager.
Smart Waitress: It's no use, sir. He can't eat it either.

"Do you realize," said a man in a cafe to a stranger at the table, "that you are reading your newspaper upside down?"

"Of course, I realize it," snapped the stranger. "Do you think it's easy?"

Two boys in the school cafeteria:
Ned: Would you like a hero sandwich?
Ted: No, I'm more the chicken type.

Mother: Eat your spinach, dear. It will put color into
    your cheeks.
Little Liz: Who wants green cheeks?

Mrs. Jones: Well, Sammy, what are you going to do
    when you get as big as your father?
Sammy: Go on a diet.

One night, Mike awoke and went to the kitchen for a
midnight snack. He opened the door of the refrigerator
and was surprised to see a rabbit.
    "How do!" said the rabbit.
    "What are you doing here?" asked Mike.
    "This is a Westinghouse, isn't it?" said the rabbit.
"And I'm just westing."

Smarty: How do you make soup gold?
Arty: I don't know. How?
Smarty: You put in fourteen carrots.

Jeff: How can you change a pumpkin into another
    vegetable?
Eff: I have no idea.
Jeff: Throw it up into the air and it will come down
    squash.

Slim: A panhandler came up to me and said he hadn't had a bite in two weeks.

Jim: Poor fellow. What did you do?

Slim: Bit him, of course!

Gert: Bert, I made two kinds of cookies today. Would you like to take your pick?

Bert: No, better use a hammer.

Al: Do you know what would happen if you ate yeast and polish?
Sal: No, Al, what?
Al: You'd rise and shine!

Beth: When does an Irish potato change its nationality?
Seth: When it's French fried.

Saul: What happens to a man who starts home to dinner and misses his train?
Paul: I don't know.
Saul: He catches it later.

Teacher: Order, children, order!
Pupil: I'll have cake and ice cream.

"Why don't you finish your alphabet soup, Frederick?" asked his mother. "There are a few letters left in your plate."

"I know but they spell spinach," answered Freddy firmly.

Gus: I saw a man-eating shark at the aquarium.
Gert: That's nothing—I saw a man eating sardines in a restaurant.

Fussy Customer: Those franks you sent me were meat at one end and corn meal at the other!
Butcher: Yes, ma'am, in these hard times it's difficult to make both ends meat.

Question: What did the ghost have for breakfast?
Answer: Ghost toasties with evaporated milk.

Question: Who's never hungry at Thanksgiving dinner?
Answer: The turkey—he's always stuffed.

Pam Pelican: That's a fine fish you have there.
Pete Pelican: Well, it sure fills the bill.

Question: What is the surest way to keep fish from
    smelling?
Answer: Just cut off their noses.

First Cannibal: Am I late for chow?
Second Cannibal: Yes, everybody's eaten.

Question: What would a cannibal be who ate his
    mother's sister?
Answer: An aunt-eater.

The teen-age cannibal turned to his date and suggested,
"Let's go on down to the old campfire and see who's
cooking!"

It was a lucky day in the cannibal village. They had
an explorer in the pot, about to be cooked. The chief
asked the victim if he had any last words to say. The
explorer gasped, "Yes. I'm smoking more now and
enjoying it less."

A cannibal mother and her little girl were watching the skies as a big airliner zoomed by. "What's that?" asked the child. "It's something like a lobster," explained the mother. "You only eat what's inside."

Sister: If you eat the rest of that pie, you'll burst.
Brother: Okay, Sis—just pass the pie and get out of the way.

Two leopards in the zoo had just finished their lunch, and one, sitting back and sighing with contentment, said: "Mm-mm-mm-mm! That just hit the right spot!"

Letter from Camp: Dear Mom & Pop, please send food packages! They only serve three meals a day here.

A waiter in a large restaurant was stricken and rushed to a nearby hospital's emergency room. On the operating table in great pain he waited for attention. An intern who recently had been to the restaurant passed by. The patient pleaded, "Doc, I'm sick. Can't you do something?" "Sorry," the intern said, "this isn't my table."

Waiter: I have boiled tongue, fried livers, and frog's legs.
Diner: Don't tell me your troubles. Just get me a cheese sandwich and a glass of milk.

Al: That pie you're eating looks good.

Pal: It *is* good.

Al: It's making my mouth water.

Pal: To show you what a good guy I am, here's a handkerchief.

Man in Restaurant: I'll have two lamb chops, and make them lean, please.

Waiter: To which side, sir?

Customer: Waiter, this soup is spoiled.
Waiter: Who told you?
Customer: A little swallow.

Mr. Dash: Waiter! I'm in a rush! Will the griddle
    cakes be long?
Waiter: No sir, round!

Question: How can you raise corned beef and cabbage?
Answer: With a knife and fork.

Connie: He's too thin.
Ronnie: Why do you say that?
Connie: His muscles look like nat bites on a piece of
    spaghetti.

Stu (sitting at dinner table where two hamburgers are
    on a platter): Father, I learned to use my head
    today.
Father: How's that, Son?
Stu: Well, I can prove that there are three hamburgers
    on this platter.
Father: All right, go ahead.
Stu (pointing at one hamburger): This is one, right?
    And this is two, okay? And don't 1 and 2 make
    3?
Father: Fine! I'll serve myself the first hamburger, your
    mother the second, and you can have the third.

A man eating dinner in a restaurant couldn't cut his steak. He complained to the waiter, "You'll have to take this meat back and get me another piece. I can't even begin to slice through it." "Sorry, sir," replied the waiter, "I can't take this back now. You've bent it."

Diner: Do you serve crabs here?
Waiter: We serve anyone; sit right down.

Waiter: We have practically everything on the menu.
Diner: So I see. Would you bring me a clean one?

Waiter: How's the soup, sir?
Diner: To tell you the truth, I'm really sorry I stirred it.

Question: When are vegetables like music?
Answer: When there are two beets to a measure.

First Lady: You know, my butcher is pretty clever.
Second Lady: What do you mean?
First Lady: He pins badges on frankfurters and sells them as police dogs.

Bill: Jake's pretty confused.
Phil: Why do you say that?
Bill: He poured ketchup on his shoelaces and tied knots in his spaghetti.

Dan: Mom made an awful mistake today and gave
    Pop some soap flakes instead of corn flakes for
    breakfast.

Ann: Was he angry?

Dan: He foamed at the mouth.

Two ants went exploring in a grocery store. First they climbed onto a shelf, then upon a box of cereal. Suddenly the first ant began running.

"Hey, wait!" the second ant shouted. "What's your hurry?"

"Can't you read?" the first ant called back.

"It says here: TEAR ALONG DOTTED LINE."

"Is she Hungary," Henry asked.

"Alaska," said Harry.

"Yes, Siam," she replied.

"All right. I'll Fiji," Henry offered.

"Oh, don't Russia," Harry admonished.

"What if she Wales?" Henry demanded.

"Give her a Canada Chile," Harry suggested.

"I'd rather have Turkey," she said, "except that I can't have any Greece."

When the waiter brought the check, Harry asked Henry, "How much has Egypt you?"

Lazy: It's easy to breakfast in bed.

Lizzy: Why do you say that?

Lazy: If you are satisfied with a few rolls and a turnover—there's nothing to it.

"Tough luck," said the egg in the monastery. "Out of the frying pan into the friar."

Little Georgie discovered a button in his salad. He remarked: "I suppose it came off while the salad was dressing."

First Cannibal: We've just captured a movie star.

Second Cannibal: Great. I was hoping for a good ham sandwich.

Question: What kind of waiter never accepts a tip?

Answer: A dumb waiter.

Question: Why is a hot dog the noblest of dogs?
Answer: Because it feeds the hand that bites it.

Ed: Who does your cooking now?
Ted: Della.
Ed: Della who?
Ted: Della Katessen.

Diner: This coffee is like mud.
Waiter: Well, it was ground this morning!

SILLY DILLIES

Question: Why did King Kong climb the Empire State
   Building?
Answer: To get his kite.

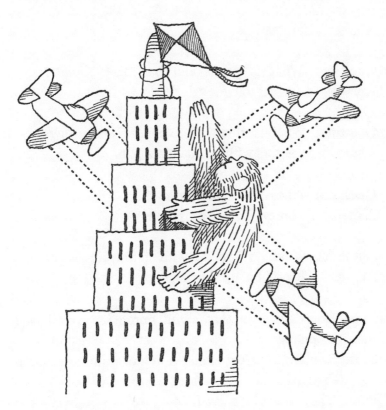

Jim: Does beer make you smart?
Tim: I don't know, but it made Budweiser!

Question: What is purple and swims around the world?
Answer: Moby grape.

Question: What are Baby Monster's parents called?
Answer: Dead and Mummy.

Question: If buttercups are yellow, what color are hiccups?
Answer: Burple.

Question: What is green and has bucket seats?
Answer: A sports olive.

Question: What is small, purple, and dangerous?
Answer: A grape with a machine gun.

Question: What is a daffy-down-dilly?
Answer: A crazy, mixed-up pickle.

Question: What do you do with a blue monster?
Answer: Cheer him up.

Sam: How'd you get that awful bump on your head?
Pam: Tomatoes.
Sam: Tomatoes? How could tomatoes raise a bump like that?
Pam: They were in a can!

Question: What do monsters do every morning at 10:30?
Answer: Take a coffin break.

Seth: Did you hear about the man who crossed a bumble bee with a doorbell?
Beth: No. What happened?
Seth: He got a humdinger.

Jean: Why did Little Liz say, "There's a grape sitting in the bathtub," when it was really a giraffe?
Jan: Why?
Jean: Little Liz is color-blind.

Luke: What do monsters eat?

Duke: I don't know, what?

Luke: They eat things, and do you know what they drink?

Duke: No.

Luke: They drink Coke—because things go better with Coke.

Rick: Do you know the recipe for a rhinoceros float?

Dick: What is it?

Rick: You take two scoops of ice cream, a rhinoceros, a dab of whipped cream, and a maraschino cherry.

Win: Here comes the parade and your sister will miss it. What is she doing?

Lyn: She's upstairs waving her hair.

Win: Gee, can't you afford a flag?

Question: What wallows in mud and carries colored eggs?

Answer: An Easter piggie.

Question: What is yellow and walks through walls?

Answer: Casper, the friendly banana.

Question: What is red and goes putt-putt-putt?

Answer: An outboard apple.

Will: Why did Santa Claus grow a garden?

Phil: I dunno.

Will: So he could Ho, Ho, Ho.

Question: What is green and dances?
Answer: Fred Asparagus.

John: What was Eve's telephone number in the Garden
    of Eden?
Don: I think it was Adam-812.

Question: What's yellow, soft, and goes round and
    round?
Answer: A long-playing omelette.

Question: What does a two-hundred-pound mouse say?
Answer: Here, Kitty, Kitty.

Question: What did the acorn say when he grew up?
Answer: Geometry (Gee, I'm a tree).

Question: What's yellow and writes?
Answer: A ball-point banana.

Question: What's big, purple, and lies across the sea from us?
Answer: Grape Britain.

Question: What has red bumps and is the fastest gun in the West?
Answer: Rootin' Tootin' Raspberry.

Question: Why did Santa Claus have only seven reindeer on Christmas Eve?
Answer: Because Comet had to stay home and clean the sink.

Question: Why is the sky so high?
Answer: So the birds won't bump their heads.

Question: What wears a black cape, flies through the night, and bites?
Answer: A mosquito in a black cape.

Question: What would you have if a bird got caught in a lawnmower?
Answer: Shredded tweet.

Question: Why is a rabbit's nose always shiny?
Answer: Because his powder puff is on the wrong end.

A mechanical man from Mars landed in Las Vegas, Nevada, and walked by a slot machine. At that moment the machine began to rumble, hit the jackpot, and out came a flood of coins. Turning to the machine, the Martian said, "You shouldn't be out with a cold like that."

Question: Who was Alexander Graham Bell Kowalski?
Answer: The first telephone Pole.

Gert: What did one balloon say to the other balloon?
Bert: What?
Gert: Nothing. Balloons can't talk.

Question: What is green and polka-dotted and grows on a vine?
Answer: An itsy bitsy, teeny weeny, polka-dotted string beany.

Question: What goes 99-thump, 99-thump, 99-thump?
Answer: A centipede with a wooden leg.

Question: What's purple and flies?
Answer: Supergrape.

Question: What is green and noisy and very dangerous?
Answer: A thundering herd of pickles.

Question: What's white outside, green inside, and hops?
Answer: A frog sandwich.

Question: What is yellow, then purple, then yellow,
   then purple, then yellow, etc.?
Answer: A banana that works nights as a grape.

A man walked into a rocket station and asked for a
ticket to the moon. "Sorry, sir," the attendant replied,
"but the moon is full."

Fred: Do you want an astronaut sandwich?
Ned: What is that?
Fred: Launch meat!

Question: What's purple and glows?
Answer: An electric grape.

Question: What's purple and conquered the world?
Answer: Alexander the Grape.

Dan: What did one volcano say to the other volcano?
Fran: I don't know. What?
Dan: Lava, come back.

Saul: What's the weather like?
Paul: It's so cloudy I can't see.

CLASSROOM CAPERS

Visiting School Board Member to student: What will
   you be when you get through school?
Student: An old, old man.

Teacher to tardy student: Why are you late?
Student: Well, I saw a sign down the street that said:
    SCHOOL AHEAD. GO SLOW!

The absent-minded professor was in his study. The telephone rang, and his assistant said, "It's a long-distance
call from San Francisco."

"That's correct," said the professor and went on
reading.

Teacher: Which one of you can use "fascinate" in a
    sentence?
Sue: I can.
Teacher: All right, Sue. Go ahead.
Sue: My coat has ten buttons, but I can only fasten
    eight.

Teacher: James, name three collective nouns.
James: The dustpan, the garbage pail, and the vacuum
    cleaner.

Teacher: Who can tell me why television is an improve-
    ment over radio?
Student: I know, teacher. Not only can you hear the
    static, but you can see it too.

The teacher spent the entire hour reading to her class
about the bison family. When she had finished, she
said, "Name some things that are very dangerous to
get near to and have horns."

Ginny spoke up without hesitation: "Automobiles."

Teacher: Oliver, why is your composition on milk only half a page long when I asked for two pages?
Oliver: Well, I wrote about condensed milk.

Teacher: Now, Peter, if I had two hamburgers and you had two hamburgers, what would we have?
Peter: Lunch.

Geology Teacher: What kind of rock is this?
Student: Oh, I'd just take it for granite.

Teacher: Class, let's discuss the grizzly bear. Does anyone know if we get fur from him?
Student: I'd get as fur from him as possible.

Stephanie's teacher came to her house to call. "I'd like to see your mother," she said when Stephanie opened the door.

"She ain't here," Stephanie answered.

"Why Stephanie, where's your grammar!" the teacher replied.

"She ain't here neither," said the girl.

The teacher was taking her class on a nature hike. As they were walking along, Bobby asked her, "Do you know what has a hundred legs, quills like a porcupine, a tail with a stinger at the end of it, six eyes, and bright green spots?"

"I've never seen such a thing, Bobby," the teacher replied.

"Well, there's one on your collar now," Bobby said.

The teacher asked the class to list, in their own opinion, the eleven greatest Americans of today. After a while, she stopped at one desk and asked, "Have you finished your list yet, Benny?"

"No, not yet, Teacher," replied Benny. "I just can't decide on a fullback."

Teacher: Courtney, spell mouse.
Courtney: *M-o-u-s.*
Teacher: But what's at the end of it?
Courtney: A tail.

Teacher: Suppose that there were people in outer space and they sent us a message. How could they tell if we had received it?
Student: They might send it collect, and see if we'd pay for it.

Teacher: Ronald! What do you mean by creeping into the classroom four minutes late?
Ronald: You said not to dare ever walk in late.

Father: Son, what is the difference between a school teacher and an engineer?
Son: One trains the mind, and the other minds the train.

Teacher: And why are you late for school, Tommy?
Tommy: There are eight children in our family, and the alarm clock was set for seven.

Teacher: Betsy, can you tell me who wrote, "Oh, Say Can You See?"

Betsy: An eye doctor.

Teacher: Sidney, what is a cannibal?

Sidney: I don't know.

Teacher: Well, if you ate your father and mother, what would you be?

Sidney: An orphan.

Teacher: How did you happen to mark this boy's paper 101%? Don't you know that nothing can be more than 100%?

Practice Teacher: Yes, but he answered one question we didn't ask!

The teacher noticed that Al had been daydreaming for a long time. She decided to get his attention. "Al," she said, "if the world is 25,000 miles around and eggs are sixty cents a dozen, how old am I?"

"Thirty-four," Al answered unhesitatingly.

The teacher blushed, then asked, "How did you ever guess?"

"Nothing to it," Al said. "My big sister is seventeen and she's only half-crazy."

The absent-minded professor's telephone rang in the middle of the night.

"Is this Hickory one-five-one-five?" the voice at the other end asked.

"No, this is Hickory fifteen-fifteen," the absent-minded professor replied.

"Sorry to have bothered you."

"Oh, that's perfectly all right," said the professor. "I had to get up anyway to answer the phone."

Teacher: Can anyone tell me what causes trees to become petrified?

George: The wind makes them rock.

Tony had trouble pronouncing the letter *R*, so his teacher gave him this sentence to practice on at home: *Ronald gave Reginald a rap in the ribs for roasting the rabbit so rare.*

A few days later she asked Tony to repeat the sentence for her. He said, "Pete gave Bob a poke in the side for not cooking the bunny enough."

Teacher: Danny, which is more important, the sun or the moon?

Danny: The moon.

Teacher: Why do you say that?

Danny: The moon shines in the night when it's dark, but the sun shines in the day when it's light anyway.

Science Teacher: When water becomes ice, what is the greatest change that takes place?

Bright Student: The price.

Science Teacher: Sidney, what's the difference between electricity and lightning?

Sidney: We have to pay for electricity.

Teacher: What is water, Sally?

Sally: It's a colorless liquid that turns black when I put my hands in it.

Father: Bob, I'm worried about your being at the foot of your class.

Bob: Don't worry about that, Pop. They teach the same thing at both ends.

Mother: I think our boy is going to be a nuclear physicist.

Father: What makes you think so?

Mother: I just spoke to his teacher, and she said he's taking up space.

Teacher: Yes, Johnny, what is it?

Johnny: I don't want to scare you, but Dad said if I didn't get better grades, someone is due for a licking.

Science Teacher: Sandy, what is an atom?

Sandy: The guy who went around with Eve.

Science Teacher: What is $Ba+Na_2$?

Student: Banana.

Teacher: Ted, I asked you to draw a horse and wagon.
    You only drew a horse.
Ted: I figured the horse would draw the wagon.

A first-grade teacher was discussing produce with her class. She asked all the boys in the class what they would raise if they were farmers. When little Billy's turn came, he replied, "I would live on the moon and raise green cheese."

"Arnold," said the teacher, "is there any connecting link between the animal kingdom and the vegetable kingdom?"
    "Yes, ma'am," answered Arnold promptly, "hash."

Teacher: Jimmy, if you had six candy bars and I asked you for three, how many would you have left?
Jimmy: Six.

A teacher asked her class for sentences using the word "beans."
    "My father grows beans," said one student.
    "My mother cooks beans," said another.
    Then a third spoke up: "We are all human beans."

Teacher: Tell me, Sammy, if you had fifteen apples and gave six of them to Jane, four to Mary and five to Nancy, what would you have then?
Sammy: Three new girl friends.

"My topic today," said the psychology professor, "will be the lie. How many of you have read the twenty-first chapter of the text?"

Nearly all the students raised their hands.

"Good," said the professor, "you're just the group I want to talk to. There are only twenty chapters in the book."

Teacher (after a discussion about ice and snow): As we walk out on a cold winter's day what do we see on every hand?
Jamie: Gloves.

Student (indignantly): I don't think I deserve a zero on this test!
Teacher: Neither do I, but it's the lowest mark I can give you.

Teacher: Roger, your hands are very dirty. What would you say if I came to school with dirty hands?
Roger: I'd be too polite to mention it.

A teacher wrote this sentence on the board and asked her class to correct it: *Girls is naturally more beautiful than boys.*

One little boy wrote: Girls is artificially more beautiful than boys.

Teacher: What pine has the longest and sharpest needles?
Linda: The porcupine.

"If I cut a beefsteak in two, and then cut the halves in two, what do I get?" asked the teacher.

"Quarters," answered the student.

"Good. And then again?"

"Eighths."

"Correct. Again?"

"Sixteenths."

"Exactly. And then?"

"Thirty-seconds."

"And once more?"

"Hamburger!" cried the boy, impatiently.

Teacher: Will you boys in the back of the room kindly stop passing notes?

Student: We're not passing notes, sir. We're playing gin.

"Amy, can you tell me how fast light travels?" the teacher asked.

"I'm not sure how fast it travels," said Amy sleepily, "but I know it gets here too early in the morning."

Teacher: Susan, I heard you have a new baby brother. What is his name?

Susan: I don't know. He won't tell me.

Teacher: Now Judy, how many fingers do you have?

Judy: Ten.

Teacher: If you lost four of them in an accident, what would you have?

Judy: No more piano lessons.

Teacher: Do camels come in flocks or herds?

Student: I think I heard my father say they come in packs.

Teacher: Albert, can you use these words in a sentence —*defeat, deduct, defense,* and *detail?*

Albert: Defeat of deduct went over defense before detail.

Teacher: Use *income* in a sentence.

Fred: I opened the door and in come the cat.

Teacher: Wrong! Try *ransom.*

Fred: I saw a skunk and ran some distance away.

Teacher: No. Try *handsome.*

Fred: Hand some candy to me.

Teacher (exasperated): Your last chance is *gruesome.*

Fred: Since last year I grew some.

Teacher: Andrew, what is a vacuum?

Andrew: I'm not quite sure how to explain it, teacher, but my father says I got one right up here in my head.

Teacher: Donald, can you give me one use for horsehide?

Donald: Well, I guess it helps to hold the horse together.

Teacher: When do the leaves begin to turn?

Student: The night before an examination.

"Now, Bill," said the teacher, "to what family does the hippopotamus belong?"

"I don't know," said Bill puzzled. "No one in our neighborhood has one."

Teacher: The Indians used beads for money.
Sid: Well, they sure must have had a hard time getting it in a gum machine!

Three absent-minded professors were talking together in a bus terminal. They got so engrossed in what they were saying that they didn't notice the bus had pulled in. As the driver sang out, "All aboard," they looked up startled and dashed from the platform. Two of them managed to hop on the bus, but the third didn't make it. As he stood sadly watching the bus disappear into the distance, a stranger tried to cheer him up, saying, "You shouldn't feel too bad. Two out of three made it, and that's a pretty good average."

The professor shook his head. "But *they* came to see *me* off."

The absent-minded professor banged his car into another at a crossroads. His was not damaged, but the other car was crushed.

"Call me up and tell me how much the repairs cost. I'll pay the bills," he told the other driver and started to pull away.

"What is your phone number?"

"It's in the phone book," the professor called back.

"But what's your name?"

"Oh, that's in the phone book, too."

Teacher: Let's take the example of the busy ant. He is busy all the time, works all day and every day. Then what happens?

Bright Student: He gets stepped on.

Teacher: What is usually used as a conductor of electricity?

Johnny: Why—er—

Teacher: Wire is right. Now tell me, what is the unit of electrical power?

Johnny: The what?

Teacher: That's absolutely correct, the watt.

The more we study, the more we know.
The more we know, the more we forget.
The more we forget, the less we know.
　　So, why study?

Teacher: Why do bees hum?
Liz: Because they don't know the words.

Tommy: What's the difference between a school teacher
    and a train?
Tony: I don't know.
Tommy: The teacher says spit that gum out, and the
    train says chew-chew.

The science teacher lecturing his class in biology said,
"Now I'll show you this frog in my pocket."
He then reached into his pocket and pulled out a
chicken sandwich. He looked puzzled for a second,
thought deeply, and said, "That's funny. I distinctly
remember eating my lunch."

Teacher: Do you know that Jones boy?
Principal: What about him?
Teacher: Not only is he the worst-behaved child in
    school, but he has a perfect attendance record.

Student: Why did they make the fingers on the Statue
    of Liberty only eleven inches long?
Teacher: One inch longer and it would have been a
    foot.

George: Teacher, would you scold someone for some-
    thing he didn't do?
Teacher: Of course not, George, why do you ask?
George: Well, I didn't do my arithmetic.

A teacher wrote on the back of one of her student's reports cards: "Amy is a good student, but she talks too much."

Amy's father signed and returned the report card with this comment: "You should meet her mother."

Teacher: Peter, can you tell me what twelve apples and twelve bananas equal?
Peter: Twenty-four banapples.

Teacher: I hope I didn't see you looking at someone else's paper, Donald.
Donald: I hope so too, teacher.

Teacher: Joe, this is the fifth day this week you've had to stay after school. What have you to say for yourself?
Joe: I'm very glad it is Friday.

Arithmetic Teacher: Sammy, if you found a quarter in one pocket, and forty cents in the other, what would you have?
Sammy: Somebody else's pants.

Ted: Why did the teacher marry the janitor?
Fred: I don't know. Why?
Ted: Because he swept her off her feet.

Teacher: How many feet are there in a yard?
Jane: It depends on how many people are standing in it.

Did you ever hear about the cross-eyed professor who had no control over his pupils?

Teacher: Jimmy, can you tell me what a waffle is?
Jimmy: Yes'm, it's a pancake with a non-skid tread.

Go to college, continue your knowledge,
To be a person smart, brave and true.
For if they can make penicillin from moldy cheese,
They surely can make something of you.

Teacher: Jennifer, can you tell me where the Red Sea is?

Jennifer: Yes, ma'am, it's on the last line of my report card.

"Oh, my goodness!" complained the absent-minded professor. He was standing in a bus, holding onto the strap with one hand while in his other hand he clutched a heavy load of books.

"Is there anything I can do to help you, sir?" asked a sympathetic fellow-passenger.

"Why, yes, there is, if you don't mind," answered the professor. "Would you please hold onto this strap for me so I can get my fare out?"

Teacher: Alice, why did you come to school with your feet so wet?

Alice: I'm wearing pumps.

Teacher: Why do we sometimes call the Middle Ages the Dark Ages?

Irving: Because they had so many knights.

Stu: Why did the little cannibal get thrown out of class?

Sue: I don't know.

Stu: Because he got caught buttering up the teacher.

Biology Teacher: What's commonly called "brain food?"

Student: Noodle soup.

Father: What is your favorite subject in school?
Ned: I guess it's gozinta.
Father: What's gozinta—a new language?
Ned: No, just gozinta: two gozinta four, four gozinta eight, eight gozinta sixteen.

Phil: Do you know what happened to the plant in the math class?
Bill: No, what?
Phil: It grew square roots.

Peter was finishing his report to the class on jet aviation. "Our modern flyers can do anything that a bird can do, and more," he announced proudly.

From the back of the room came a whispered: "I'd like to see one sleeping on a telephone wire with his head tucked under his wing!"

Bob: Oh, great! Teacher said we would have a test today, rain or shine.
Rob: What's so great about that?
Bob: It's snowing.

Little Boy (to teacher): That's my dad's signature on my excuse, teacher, and here's the tracing to prove it.

Frank: What are you majoring in at college?
Hank: Cycle-ology.
Frank: Oh, are you going to be a psychoanalyst?
Hank: No, I'm going to repair bicycles.

Teacher: What was the most wonderful accomplish-
ment of the Romans?
Oliver: Learning Latin.

SAGE SIGNS

Sign at a roadside bait stand:
WORMS WITH FISH APPEAL.

Sign in front of a house:
ANYONE IS WELCOME TO BORROW OUR LAWN
MOWER, AS LONG AS HE DOESN'T TAKE IT OUT OF
OUR YARD.

Student's creed:
LAUGH AND THE CLASS LAUGHS WITH YOU, BUT
YOU STAY AFTER SCHOOL ALONE.

Sign in a service station:
WE COLLECT TAXES—FEDERAL, STATE, AND LOCAL.
WE ALSO SELL GASOLINE AS A SIDELINE.

Sign in another service station:
WE ARE THE FIRST STATION IN THIS TOWN TO
BE SELLING THE NEW GAS THAT PUTS A RABBIT
IN YOUR TANK; IT'S FOR SHORT HOPS.

Sign in a store selling tropical fish:
 WET PETS.

Sign on a Daffy Dairy Delivery truck:
 YOU CAN'T BEAT OUR MILK, BUT YOU CAN WHIP
 OUR CREAM.

Sign in a restaurant window:
 T-BONE 50¢
 (then underneath in fine print): WITH MEAT $5.00

Sign in police station:

THIRTY DAYS HATH SEPTEMBER, APRIL, JUNE AND THE SPEED OFFENDER.

One day a man was driving along a dirt road in the jungle when he came upon a strange sign. It read:

CANNIBAL VILLAGE, 500 YARDS.

He drove on, finally reached the village, and there he saw another sign. It read:

OUR SLOGAN—TAKE THE BUS AND LEAVE THE DRIVER TO US.

Sign at an intersection:

CROSS ROAD
BETTER HUMOR IT

Street sign:

TO AVOID THAT RUN DOWN FEELING, LOOK BOTH WAYS BEFORE CROSSING.

TRICKS OF THE TRADES

Lew: Did you hear about the angel who lost his job?
Sue: No, what happened?
Lew: He had harp failure.

"One thing I just don't understand," the judge said to the burglar standing before him. "Why did you break into the same store three nights in a row?"

"Your Honor, it's like this," the burglar answered. "I picked out a dress for my wife, and I had to change it twice."

Voice on the Phone: Is this the game warden?

Game Warden: Yes, it is.

Voice: Thank goodness, I have the right person at last. Would you please give me some suggestions for a child's birthday party?

Don: I understand your brother had an accident in the Submarine Service—what happened?

Ron: Well, he never got over the habit of opening the windows at night when he went to bed.

First Gardener: I used to work with thousands of men under me.

Second Gardener: Really?

First Gardener: Yep, I cut the grass in a cemetery.

A man walked up to the General Delivery window at the post office, where a new clerk was busy sorting letters.

"Any mail for Mike Howe?" the man bellowed.

The clerk ignored him, and the man repeated his question in an even louder voice. Without looking up, the clerk replied, "Not for your cow, or your horse either."

Mr. Jet: What are you doing nowadays?
Mr. Wet: I'm with the water works.
Mr. Jet: I see. Well, drop in some day.

A local newspaper recently printed an article in which the following statement appeared: "Mr. Sean O'Reilly is a new defective on the police force."

In the following issue, to correct the error, the paper announced: "Mr. Sean O'Reilly is a new detective on the police farce."

First Safecracker: I guess I need eyeglasses.
Second Safecracker: What makes you think so?
First Safecracker: Well, I was twirling the knobs of a
    safe, and an orchestra began to play.

Boy (in a dime store): Who's in charge of the nuts?
Clerk: Wait just a minute, and I'll take care of you.

A man was walking along the beach during high tide and decided he wanted a bucket of salt water. As a joke, the lifeguard charged him a quarter. Returning at low tide, the man said to the lifeguard, "Boy, you sure must have had good business today!"

Harry: Wait a minute, do you mean to say Tony gave
    up his job as a traveling salesman just to please
    his wife?
Henry: Yes. It seems that she wanted her Tony home
    permanent.

Olly: My dad makes faces all day.
Polly: Why does he do that?
Olly: Because he works in a clock factory.

Question: Why is your heart like a policeman?
Answer: Because it follows a regular beat.

A lady walked into a shoe store and asked to be waited on. The salesman said, "Of course, miss, and what sort of shoe are you looking for?"

"I would like to buy a pair of alligator shoes," the lady said.

The salesman replied, "And what size does he take?"

Prisoner: The judge sent me here for the rest of my life.
Warden: Got any complaints?
Prisoner: Do you call breaking rocks with a hammer, *rest?*

Saul: I saw you pushing your bicycle to work.
Paul: Yes, I was so late I didn't even have time to get on.

Kitty: Did Gertrude inherit her beauty?
Catty: Yes, her uncle left her a drugstore.

Question: What time would it be if a lion ate the postmaster?
Answer: 8 P.M. (ate p.m.).

Sam: Did you hear about the man who fell into the lens-grinding machine?

Pam: What happened to him?

Sam: He made a spectacle of himself.

Fred: Did you hear what the burglar gave his wife for her birthday?

Ed: No, what?

Fred: A stole.

Conductor: Will you please open the piano?

Pianist: I can't. The keys are on the inside.

Question: What sort of offspring does a stupid florist have?

Answer: Blooming idiots.

Teacher: Why is paper money more valuable than coins?

Student: Well, when you put it in your pocket, you double it, and when you take it out, you find it still in creases.

Warden: Men, today marks my fifteenth anniversary as head of this prison, and I'd like all of you to join me in celebrating. What kind of party would you suggest?

Prisoners (in chorus): Open house.

Employer: Why did you come back today? Didn't you get my letter saying that you were fired?

Employee: Yes, but on the envelope it said, "After five days return." So, here I am.

Husband: I've just discovered oil.

Wife: That's wonderful. Now we can get a new car.

Husband: We'd better get the old car fixed first—that's where the oil is coming from.

Reilly: It's nice to be back from my vacation. We had awful weather. It rained most of the time.

Smiley: It couldn't have been too bad. That's a nice tan you have.

Reilly: Tan nothing, that's rust.

Will: I'm a conductor.

Phil: You are? What kind? Music conductor or train conductor?

Will: Neither. I was struck by lightning.

Sculptor: Do you know that it took me half my life to realize that I had no artistic ability?

Acquaintance: So then you gave it up?

Sculptor: Oh, no, by then I was so famous I couldn't afford to give it up.

Question: Why do gardeners hate weeds?

Answer: Because if you give them an inch they'll take a yard.

A camp counselor was supposed to get some work out of the twelve boys lined up in front of him. They weren't as enthusiastic as he thought they should be, so he tried using psychology.

"I've got a nice, easy job for the laziest man here," he said. "Will the laziest boy raise his hand?"

Eleven hands went up.

"Why didn't you raise your hand?" he asked the twelfth.

"Too much trouble," drawled the boy.

Chef: What is the best thing to put in a pie?

Apprentice: Your teeth.

A florist received an outraged telephone call from a man who had moved his restaurant to a new spot in town. The restaurant owner had been sent a funeral wreath along with a card that read: SINCEREST SYM-PATHIES.

The florist realized that he must have mixed up two orders and shuddered to think of the flowers that should have gone to the restaurant man. He had sent to the funeral a clover design of red roses across which was a bright green ribbon bearing the inscription: BEST OF LUCK IN YOUR NEW LOCATION.

Ronnie: How is your typing speed coming along, Connie?
Connie: Fine. Now I can make fifteen mistakes a minute.

"I started in life without a penny in my pocket," bragged Mr. Briggs.
"And I," replied Mr. Braggs, "began life without a pocket."

Father to Son: Well, what are you going to be when you grow up?
Son: An Arctic explorer.
Father: But that's a life full of hardship.
Son: Sure, but you don't ever have to wash your face!

Harry: Hey, Larry, if an athlete gets athlete's foot, what does an astronaut get?
Larry: Missile toe, I guess.

Joe: Can you remember the name of that guy who used to work in the side show shaking his right arm down a lion's throat?

Moe: I forget his real name, but they call him "Lefty" now.

Jim: I'm sorry to hear that your factory was burned down. By the way, what did you manufacture?

Tim: Fire extinguishers.

"Dad, is it correct to say that a rail layer lays rails?"

"Yes, son."

"And a cake mixer mixes cakes?"

"Yes, son."

"And a weight lifter lifts weights?"

"Yes, son."

"Then does a shoplifter lift shops?"

The barber looked at his teen-age customer's slick, plastered-down hair and asked, "Do you just want me to cut it or do you want me to check the oil too?"

A man selling vacuum cleaners knocked on the door of a farmhouse. When the farmer's wife opened it, the salesman said, "Madam, I want to show you something you'll never forget."

Before she could say a word, he threw a sack of dry leaves onto her clean floor.

"Now," he continued, "I want to make a bargain with you. If this latest model Electroclean vacuum cleaner doesn't pick up every bit of that mess, I'll eat it."

"Here's a spoon," the farmer's wife said. "We don't have electricity."

A woman ran into a hardware store and asked to be waited on in a hurry. "Give me a mouse trap quickly, please," she said. "I have only two minutes to catch a train."

"Sorry," replied the clerk. "We don't have any that big."

A lady went into a clothing store and asked, "May I try on that dress in the window?"

"Well," replied the sales clerk doubtfully, "don't you think it would be better to use the dressing room?"

Ted: I don't know whether to take a job in a barbershop or to spend my time writing novels.
Ed: Toss a coin—heads or tales.

Mr. Fix-It: Lady, I'm the piano tuner.
Mrs. Smith: I didn't send for a piano tuner.
Mr. Fix-It: I know it, lady, but your neighbor did.

Hank: What do you sell?
Frank: Salt.
Hank: I'm a salt seller, too.
Frank: Shake.

A woman had just about finished looking at all the trunks in the luggage department. When there was only one left, she said to the clerk, "I'm not going to buy anything right now. I'm only looking for a friend."

The tired clerk replied, "I'd be glad to let you look in this last one if you think that's where she is."

Personnel Officer: I'm afraid that young man I hired last week isn't honest.
Supervisor: Oh, you shouldn't judge by appearance.
Personnel Officer: I'm not. I happen to be judging by disappearances in this case.

Mr. Hobbins: My boss has taken up the art of tumbling.

Mr. Robbins: Why did he do that?

Mr. Hobbins: Because he has a gall bladder condition. He heard that a rolling boss gathers no stones.

She: What job do you hold in the army?

Recruit: I'm the corps optometrist.

She: What do you do?

Recruit: My job is to cut out eyes in potatoes.

Ef: I hear the men are striking.

Jeff: What for?

Ef: Shorter hours.

Jeff: Good for them. I always did think sixty minutes was too long for an hour.

Jane: Knock, knock!

John: Who's there?

Jane: The Avon lady. Your doorbell's broken.

Fred: Why does Bernie work as a baker?

Ted: I suppose he kneads the dough.

HISTORICAL HOWLERS

An emperor of Persia had just started ruling his country. He was very kind and lenient. He loved wild animals and let them run loose throughout his domain. The people got so annoyed. They revolted and overthrew their leader. That was the first time in history that the reign was called on account of game.

On election day a man in a small South American village was given a sealed envelope at the polling place and told to drop it into the ballot box. He started to tear it open when a South American polling commissioner screamed, "What are you doing?" The man answered, "I only wanted to see for whom I'm voting." "Are you crazy?" the official asked. "This is a secret ballot!"

The thunder god went for a ride on his favorite filly.
  "I'm Thor," he cried.
  The horse replied, "You forgot your thaddle, thilly."

Paul: Have you heard about the Revolutionary patriot
    who trained a chicken to find British Loyalists?
Nathan: No, I haven't.
Paul: Haven't you ever heard of chicken cacciatore?

Mack: What did George Washington's father say when
    George brought home his report card?
Jack: What?
Mack: Why did you go down in History?

Question: Why couldn't King Arthur find his page?
Answer: Because he had closed his book.

One of King Arthur's knights charged into an inn. A fierce storm raged outside. "Can you lend me a horse?" he asked the innkeeper. "My steed is too weary to go another step." "Sir Knight," the innkeeper replied, "I have no horse. The only animal I have is that big, old dog in the corner." "Very well," said the knight, "I shall ride him." "Oh no, sire!" the innkeeper cried. "I wouldn't send a knight out on a dog like this."

General Custer: I hear your name is Sitting Bull.
Sitting Bull: Yes.
General Custer: Then, why aren't you sitting?
Sitting Bull: I'm on vacation.

Question: Why does Uncle Sam wear red-white-and-blue suspenders?
Answer: To hold his pants up.

Question: What instructions did Noah give his sons about fishing off the ark?
Answer: Go easy on the bait, boys. I only have two worms.

Question: What fruit lasted the longest in Noah's ark?
Answer: The preserved pairs.

Teacher: What can you tell me about the great chemists of the seventeenth century?
Student: They are all dead.

Teacher: What did Paul Revere say after his famous ride?
Student: Whoa!

Miss Brown: Without oxygen, human life would be impossible. This important gas was discovered in 1773.
Irving: Miss Brown, what did people breathe before oxygen was discovered?

Teacher: Can any of you tell me anything of importance that did not exist fifty years ago?
Student: *Me*.

Question: What bus crossed the ocean?
Answer: Columbus.

It's hard to believe that just one hundred years ago people were crossing the country in wagon trains. Today we can shoot a rocket into space at 25,000 miles an hour, and nobody's watching. They're all inside looking at "Wagon Train."

Question: When is a piece of wood like a king?
Answer: When it is made into a ruler.

Sue: I'm taking Ancient History.
Lou: So am I. Let's get together and talk over old
     times.

Question: For how long a period of time did Cain hate
     his brother?
Answer: As long as he was Abel.

Question: Who was the biggest bandit in history?
Answer: Atlas—he held up the world.

Question: Why did the pioneers cross the country in
     covered wagons?
Answer: Because they didn't want to wait forty years
     for a train or a hundred years for a plane.

Question: If April showers bring May flowers, what
     do May flowers bring?
Answer: Pilgrims.

Question: Where did the Pilgrim Fathers stand when
     they landed on Plymouth Rock?
Answer: On their feet.

ELEPHANTS, Elephants, elephants

Question: What's gray, has four legs, and a trunk?
Answer: A mouse going on a trip.

Question: How does an elephant get down from a tree?
Answer: He climbs out on a leaf and waits for autumn.

Question: Why did the elephant lie in the middle of the sidewalk?
Answer: To trip the ants.

Fred: What's the difference between a loaf of bread and an elephant?
Ed: I don't know. What?
Fred: Well, if you don't know the difference, I'm certainly not going to send *you* to the store for a loaf of bread.

Question: What do you do with old bowling balls?
Answer: Give them to the elephants to shoot marbles.

Question: Why did the elephant paint her head yellow?
Answer: She wanted to see if blondes had more fun.

Tina: Why does an elephant have a trunk?
Nina: I don't know. Why?
Tina: He would look mighty silly with a glove compartment.

Question: Why did the elephant paint himself all different colors?
Answer: So he could hide in a package of M-&-Ms.

Question: Which takes longer to get ready for a trip—
a rooster or an elephant?
Answer: The elephant, because he has to take a trunk
while the rooster takes only his comb.

Question: What words do you use to scold an elephant?
Answer: Tusk! Tusk!

Question: How do you tell an elephant from a monster?
Answer: An elephant remembers.

Fred: Have a peanut.

Ed: No, thanks, they're fattening.

Fred: Can you prove it?

Ed: Have you ever seen a skinny elephant?

Question: How do you get an elephant into a popcorn box?

Answer: You don't. They only come in Crackerjacks.

Question: Why can't an elephant ride a bicycle?

Answer: Because he has no thumb to ring the bell.

Question: Why is an elephant gray, large, and wrinkled?

Answer: Because if he were small, white, and round he would be an aspirin.

Question: What's gray on the inside and clear on the outside?

Answer: An elephant in a Baggie.

Question: What did the grape say when the elephant stepped on it?

Answer: Nothing, it just let out a little whine.

Tina: More than six thousand elephants go each year to make piano keys.

Nina: Really! It's remarkable what animals can be trained to do.

Question: Why do elephants have wrinkled ankles?

Answer: They lace their sneakers too tightly.

Question: How do you get down off an elephant?
Answer: You don't. You get down off a duck.

Question: Why does an elephant have cracks between his toes?
Answer: To carry his library card.

Question: Why are elephants so wrinkled?
Answer: Did you ever try to iron one?

Question: Why aren't elephants allowed on the beach?
Answer: Because they can't keep their trunks up.

Question: How can you tell an elephant is in your
refrigerator?
Answer: You can see his footprints in the butter.

Question: Why did the elephant sit on a marshmallow?
Answer: To keep from falling into the cocoa.

Question: How can you tell when there is an elephant
under your bed?
Answer: When you are nearly touching the ceiling.

Question: How do you keep an elephant from charg-
ing?
Answer: Take away his credit card.

Question: What can you say about nine elephants wearing pink sneakers and one elephant wearing blue?
Answer: Nine out of ten elephants wear pink sneakers.

Question: What time is it when an elephant sits on a
fence?
Answer: Time to buy a new fence.

Question: What is the difference between an elephant
and a jar of peanut butter?
Answer: The elephant doesn't stick to the roof of your
mouth.

Question: Why did the elephants quit the circus?
Answer: They got tired of working for peanuts.

Bill: What's the difference between an elephant and a matterbaby?
Jill: What's a matterbaby?
Bill: Nothing, dear. What's the matter with you?

Question: What weighs four thousand pounds and sings?
Answer: Harry Elefonte.

Question: How can you tell when there is an elephant in your sandwich?

Answer: When it is too heavy to lift.

Tina: What's the difference between a lemon, an elephant, and a tube of glue?

Nina: I give up.

Tina: You can squeeze a lemon, but you can't squeeze an elephant.

Nina: What about the tube of glue?

Tina: That's where you get stuck.

Question: What is the difference between an elephant and a blueberry?

Answer: A blueberry is blue.

Question: What is the difference between a flea and an elephant?

Answer: An elephant can have fleas, but a flea can't have elephants.

Question: What did Tarzan say when he saw the elephants coming?

Answer: Here come the elephants.

Question: What did Tarzan say when he saw the elephants coming with sunglasses on?

Answer: Nothing. He didn't recognize them.

Question: How do you lift an elephant?

Answer: Put him on an acorn and let it grow.

Recipe for Elephant Stew

One elephant, two rabbits (optional), salt, and pepper. Cut the elephant into small bite-size pieces. This should take about two months. Add enough brown gravy to cover. Cook over kerosene stove for about four weeks at 465 degrees. This will serve 3800 people. If more are expected, two rabbits may be added, but do this only if necessary because most people do not like to find hares in their stew.

Tina: Why did the elephants paint their toenails red?
Nina: I don't know. Why?
Tina: So they could hide in the strawberry patch. Did you ever see an elephant in a strawberry patch?
Nina: No!
Tina: That proves it works.

Question: What did the elephant say to the platypus?
Answer: I never forget a face, but with yours I'll make an exception.

Question: What did the elephant think of the grape's house?
Answer: De-vine.

Question: Why do elephants wear dark glasses?
Answer: If you had all those jokes told about you, you wouldn't want to be recognized either!

Question: How is an elephant like a Volkswagen?
Answer: The trunk is in front.

Question: How do you fit five elephants into a Volks-
    wagen?
Answer: Two in the front, two in the back, and one in
    the glove compartment.

IS THERE A DOCTOR IN THE HOUSE?

Question: When is an operation funny?
Answer: When it leaves the patient in stitches.

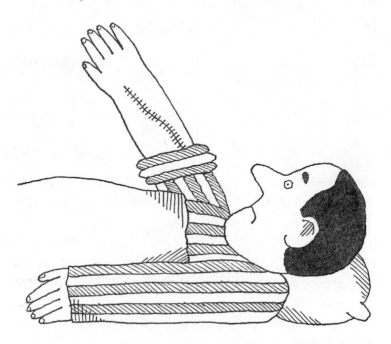

"There's nothing wrong with you," said the psychiatrist to his patient. "Why you're as sane as I am."

"But, doctor," cried the patient, as he brushed madly at his clothes, "it's these butterflies! They're all over me."

"For heaven's sake," cried the doctor, "don't brush them off on me."

Billy: What did the tonsil say to the other tonsil?
Willy: I don't know, what?
Billy: Get dressed. Doc is taking us out tonight.

Patient: This ointment makes my arm smart!
Doctor: Why not rub some on your head?

Lily: When do broken bones make themselves useful?
Milly: I give up. When?
Lily: When they begin to knit.

Jim: Isn't Mother Nature wonderful?
Slim: Why do you say that?
Jim: Well, millions of years ago she didn't know man was going to invent glasses, yet look how conveniently she placed his ears!

Sam: When they take your appendix out, it is an appendectomy; when they remove your tonsils from your throat, it is a tonsillectomy. What is it when you remove growth from your head?
Pam: I don't know.
Sam: A haircut.

Patient: Doctor, I can't sleep at night. I keep having the same dream about a door with a sign. I push and push but I can never get it open.

Doctor: What does it say?

Patient: Pull

Patient: Will I be able to read when I get my glasses?

Doctor: You certainly will, my boy.

Patient: Well, that's fine. I never knew how before.

Mack: What did the Pilgrims come over on?
Jack: The *Mayflower*.
Mack: What did the midgets come on?
Jack: Shrimp boats.
Mack: And what did the doctors come on?
Jack: Blood vessels.

Prison Guard: Sir, I want to report that twelve prisoners have just broken out.
Warden: Sound the alarm, blow the whistle, issue machine guns!
Prison Guard: Let me call the doctor first, it looks as if it might be measles.

Bert: Billy sure is a blockhead.
Gert: Why do you say that?
Bert: The other day he found a feather in his bed and he was sure he had chicken pox.

Bob: Why is a dentist like a gas-station attendant?
Rob: I don't know. Why?
Bob: They both run filling stations.

Two men were sitting in the doctor's office, and after a while they decided to talk.

"I'm aching from arthritis," said one man.

"Glad to meet you," said the other. "I'm Willy from Philly."

Dr. Nesbitt, a veterinarian, was also the county sheriff. Late one night he had an urgent phone call. "Shall I bring my medicine kit or my handcuffs?" Dr. Nesbitt asked sleepily.

"Both!" answered the voice on the other end of the line. "I can't get my dog's mouth open, and there's a burglar in it."

Doctor: Have your eyes ever been checked?
Patient: No. They've always been brown.

Doctor: What's your average weight?
Patient: Have no idea.
Doctor: Well, what's the most you ever weighed?
Patient: I guess about 150 pounds.
Doctor: All right. What's the least you ever weighed?
Patient: Seven pounds four ounces.

Doctor: You know there's an epidemic in this town, don't you? What are you doing to protect your family?
Hillbilly: Well, we got one of these here sanitary cups, and we all drink out of it.

Dentist: What kind of filling do you want in your tooth?
Young Patient: Chocolate.

One day a doctor went out on a sick call in a rural community. As he walked up to the house, he noticed a deep well in the yard. He walked over, but tripped on a stone and fell into the well. The moral of this story: Doctor, tend the sick and leave the well alone.

Lou: Do you know what the man got who invented Metrecal?
Sue: No, what?
Lou: The no-belly prize.

Old Friend: Where have you been the last few years?
Student: At the university taking Medicine.
Old Friend: Were you finally cured?

An elderly couple took their young son to a doctor.

Doctor: What's wrong with him?

Father: He thinks he is a chicken.

Doctor: How long has he been thinking this?

Mother: About ten years.

Doctor: Why didn't you bring him in to see me before this?

Father: Because we needed the eggs!

A man walked into a veterinarian's office with his sick rabbit. He said, "I can't understand it, doc. He looks awful, and I don't feed him anything but goat's milk." The vet's reply was, "That's the trouble. Don't you know you're not supposed to use that greasy kid stuff on your hare?"

Question: What is the difference between a hill and a pill?
Answer: A hill is hard to get up. A pill is hard to get down.

Doctor: Well, how's your cold today?
Patient: Worse than ever.
Doctor: Did you follow the treatment I prescribed and drink the orange juice after the hot bath?
Patient: No, after the hot bath, I couldn't get the orange juice down.

Fred: He's an MD.
Ed: A doctor?
Fred: No, Mentally Deficient.

Gil: What time do most people go to the dentist?
Jill: I don't know. What time?
Gil: At tooth-hurty.

Doctor: The check you gave me last month came back.
Patient: So did the pain.

A man visited a psychiatrist because he thought he was a canary.

A few months later, his wife phoned to inquire how her husband was coming along. "Fine," was the reply. "Lately, I haven't heard a peep out of him."

The psychiatrist was questioning his patient. "Do you ever hear voices without being able to tell who is speaking, or where the voices are coming from?" he asked.

"Yes, sir," the patient answered.

"And when does this occur?" asked the doctor.

"When I answer the telephone."

Doctor: Are you still taking the cough medicine I gave you?

Patient: No, I tasted it and decided that I'd rather have the cough.

Patient: I know I wasn't dead because I was hungry and my feet were cold.

Doctor: What does that prove?

Patient: If I'd gone to heaven, I wouldn't be hungry, and if I hadn't, my feet wouldn't be cold.

"There's nothing wrong with Lily's eyes," the optometrist assured the father of the teen-ager.

"Well, then what's the problem?" asked the father.

"The only trouble is that her pigtails are too tight," replied the doctor.

Tim: Do you know what happened when the dentist married the manicurist?

Jim: No, what?

Tim: They fought tooth and nail ever after.

Doctor: Don't you know my hours are from 2 to 5 P.M.?

Patient: Yes, but the dog that bit me didn't.

Question: Why do doctors and nurses wear masks?

Answer: So that if someone makes a mistake, no one will know who did it.

Doctor: What's that miserly patient complaining about now?

Nurse: He says he got well before all the medicine was used up!

Bill: What can you give away and still keep?

Phil: I have no idea. What?

Bill: A cold.

Don: One of my pigs was sick, so I gave him a piece of sugar.

John: Why did you do that?

Don: Haven't you ever heard of sugar-cured ham?

Doctor: Are you taking care of your cold?

Patient: I've had it a week and it seems as good as new.

Sam: Hey, Dad, that man wasn't a painless dentist like he advertised.

Father: Why? Did he hurt you?

Sam: No, but he yelled when I bit his thumb, just like any other dentist.

Mrs. Brill: My son swallowed a pen.

Doctor: I'll be there soon, but what are you doing in the meantime?

Mrs. Brill: Using a pencil.

Mother: Good gracious, Billy, I forgot to shake the bottle before I gave you that medicine.

Billy: Don't worry, Mom. I'll just turn a few handsprings.

Patient: Doctor, do you think cranberries are healthy?

Doctor: Well, I've never heard one complain.

Doctor: Ask the accident victim his name so we can notify his family.

Nurse (after consulting the patient): He says his family already knows.

Patient: I feel funny, doctor. What shall I do?

Doctor: Go on television.

Dan: What are you taking for your cold?

Fran: What will you give me?

Two men found themselves seated next to one another in the recovery room of a blood donation center. One was a New Yorker, the other, an Apache Indian. After staring at the Indian for a few minutes, the New Yorker could contain his curiosity no longer. "Are you really a full-blooded Indian?" he inquired. "Not really," replied the Apache, "I'm one pint short."

Gil: Have you heard about the new doctor doll?

Bill: Nope.

Gil: You wind it up, and it operates on batteries.

A little girl went to the dentist to have a tooth pulled. Noticing that the youngster was frightened, the dentist gave her a tranquilizer.

"Feel braver now?" the dentist asked.

"You said it," the girl replied. "I'd like to see anybody try to yank out my tooth now."

Dentist: Please stop screaming! I haven't even touched your tooth yet.
Patient: I know, but you're stepping on my foot.

JEST FOR FUN

Two little girls became very intrigued with a small turtle in a bowl. One morning when they went to see him, he had gone into his shell. "Come quickly, Mummy!" the older girl cried. "He has gone and has forgotten to take his umbrella with him."

Twinkle, twinkle, little star.
How I wonder what you are.
I wish I may, I wish I might—
Aw shucks, it's a satellite!

Newspaper advertisement:
LOST—WRIST WATCH BY A LADY WITH A CRACKED FACE.

Dave: I'm stronger than Tarzan.
Dick: No, you're not.
Dave: Yes, I am.
Dick: How do you know?
Dave: I can beat my chest without hollering.

Just to make sure, the vacationer asked the native Floridian if there were any alligators around. Reassured that there were none, he dove into the water only to hear the man on the beach shout, "Alligators never come around here—the sharks scare them away."

Jerry: Do you know what happened to the worm that joined the army?

Johnny: No, tell me about it.

Jerry: They put him in the apple corps.

Nit: Can you tell me what one herring said to the other herring?

Wit: Be thy brother's kipper!

Kim: Why don't you like girls?

Tim: They're too biased.

Kim: Biased? What do you mean by that?

Tim: It's bias this and bias that till I'm broke.

Customer: How much is that bird?

Clerk: Ten dollars, ma'am.

Customer: I'll take it. Will you charge it and send me
    the bill?

Clerk: Sorry, ma'am, you'll have to take the whole bird.

Once there were four boys sitting in a tree.

Unfortunately, one fell out.

Fortunately, there was a haystack below him.

Unfortunately, there was a pitchfork in the haystack.

Fortunately, he missed the pitchfork.

Unfortunately, he missed the haystack.

Mrs. Busy: Is your new home warm?

Mrs. Body: It should be. The painter gave it two coats last month.

Saul: How were Adam and Eve prevented from gambling?

Paul: Their paradise was taken from them.

Knock, knock.
Who's there?
Banana.
Banana who?
Banana, Banana.

Knock, knock.
Who's there?
Banana.
Banana who?
Banana, Banana.

Knock, knock.
Who's there?
Orange.
Orange who?
Orange you glad I'm not Banana?

Knock, knock.
Who's there?
Tuba.
Tuba who?
Tuba-toothpaste.

Knock, knock.
Who's there?
Marsha.
Marsha who?
Marsha-mallow.

Knock, knock.
Who's there?
Divan.
Divan who?
Divan the bathtub; I'm dwoning.

Knock, knock.
Who's there?
Oswald.
Oswald who?
Oswald my gum.

Two elderly ladies got on a plane. One went up to the pilot and said, "Sir, please don't go faster than the speed of sound. Mrs. Jones and I want to talk all the way."

A student's complaint:
Our teachers have gone to college for years to understand us, but they expect us to understand them without any education at all.

Many young ladies seem to have the notion that a woman's work is done when she sweeps down the aisle.

"Did you hear the story about Algy and the bear?" John asked Peter.

"It's very short. It goes like this: Algy met a bear; the bear was bulgy; the bulge was Algy."

Mrs. Biddle was walking down the street one day carrying a small box with holes punched in the top.

"What's in that box?" Mrs. Riddle asked.

"A cat," Mrs. Biddle answered.

"What for?"

"I've been dreaming about mice at night, and I'm scared of mice. The cat is to catch them."

"But the mice you dream about are imaginary," said Mrs. Riddle.

Mrs. Biddle turned to her friend and whispered, "So is the cat."

Question: Why should fish be better educated than bugs?

Answer: Because they live in schools.

Knock, knock.
Who's there?
Honeydew and cantaloupe.
Honeydew and cantaloupe who?
Honeydew you love me; we cantaloupe now.

Parents spend the first part of a child's life urging him to walk and talk, and the rest of his childhood making him sit down and keep quiet.

Fred: Look at that tumbledown shack! I wonder what
keeps it together?
Ed: The termites are holding hands.

A lady called the operator soon after a new telephone
was installed in her house.

"My telephone cord is too long," she said. "I wonder
if you could help me out? Will you just pull a little
from your end?"

A sailor rushed up to the officer of the deck in such excitement that he stammered and stuttered. The officer lost patience with him and said, "Sing it out, sailor, sing it out!"

The sailor drew a deep breath and began to sing:

"Should auld acquaintance be forgot and never brought to mind? The admiral's fallen overboard—he's half a mile behind!"

Missionary: Why are you giving me the once over?
Cannibal: I am the food inspector.

Paul: What's the difference between a tuna fish and a
    piano?
Saul: I don't know.
Paul: You can't tune a fish.

The outer space creature was making his way down the road when he met a lady carrying a transistor television set. He looked at her in surprise and said, "Earthwoman, why do you carry your child around without a coat?"

Two goats were snooping around the back lot of a Hollywood movie studio when they came upon a can of film. One goat devoured the can and the film. His companion watched him and, when he had finished, asked, "How was it?" The first goat replied, "Frankly, the book was better."

Three slightly deaf old men met on the street one day.

"Windy, isn't it?" said one.

"No, Thursday," said the second.

"So am I," said the third. "Let's all go and have a cup of coffee."

Jim: Four men fell in the water, but only one of them got his hair wet.

Tim: Why?

Jim: Three of them were bald.

Irv: Your pants look rather sad today.

Merv: What do you mean?

Irv: Depressed.

Question: What happens when a melancholy microbe shoots himself with penicillin?

Answer: He dies in vein.

Mr. and Mrs. Bright had just started taking French lessons.

"Why are you doing that?" a friend asked.

"We just adopted a French baby," Mrs. Bright replied, "and we want to know what he's saying as soon as he learns to talk."

"We will now read from the Book of Numbers," said the preacher, as he opened the telephone directory.

Don: There are several things I can always count on.

Ron: What are they?

Don: My fingers.

A lady walked into the market and asked the butcher for a side of beef. The butcher went into the back room, came back leading a cow, and said, "Which side, Lady?"

Father Bear: Someone has been eating my porridge.
Mother Bear: Someone has been eating my porridge.
Baby Bear: Someone has been eating my porridge.
Grandmother Bear: I wish you'd all stop jumping to conclusions. I haven't even served the porridge yet!

Two Indian medicine men had been praying to their rain god for weeks with no results. Said one to the other, "I'm afraid our idol is idle."

Sal: Our dining room table goes back to Louis the Fourteenth.

Al: That's nothing, our whole dining room set goes back to the store the thirteenth.

Husband (phoning his wife from the office at 4 P.M.): I've got two tickets for the theater.

Wife: Wonderful! I'll start getting dressed.

Husband: Yes, do. The tickets are for tomorrow night.

Harry: I guess my pen will just have to go on itching.

Barry: Why?

Harry: I'm all out of scratch paper.

A boy walked into a drugstore and asked for a bowl of Pepsi. The soda jerk said, "Sorry, we don't sell Pepsi by the bowl." The boy began to protest noisily, and to quiet him down, the soda jerk said, "Okay, okay, you can have it in a bowl." The boy took a dead canary out of his pocket, put it in the Pepsi and said, "Come alive."

Question: What did the dirt say when it rained?

Answer: If this keeps up, my name is mud.

Pa: When I was a kid, ten cents was a lot of money.

Ma: How dimes have changed!

Stu: Did you hear about the rope joke?

Sue: No.

Stu: Then just skip it.

The policeman brought four boys before the judge. "They were causing an awful lot of commotion at the zoo, Your Honor," he said.

"Boys," said the judge sternly, "I never like to hear reports of juvenile delinquency. Now I want each one of you to tell me your name, and what you were doing wrong."

"My name is George," said the first boy, "and I threw peanuts into the elephant pen."

"My name is Pete," said the second boy, "and I threw peanuts into the elephant pen."

"My name is Dick," said the third boy, "and I threw peanuts into the elephant pen."

"My name is Peanuts," said the fourth boy.

Paul: What do you get when you cross a movie with a swimming pool?
Saul: I don't know. What?
Paul: A dive-in-theater.

Pity the poor little firefly.
He must have lost his mind,
To blunder through existence
With his headlight on behind.

Humpty Dumpty sat on a wall.
Humpty Dumpty had a great fall.
All the King's horses and all the King's men
Came and ate scrambled eggs.

Olly: Tom was cleaning a cannon when he was in the
     service, and it suddenly went off.

Molly: What happened to him?

Olly: He was discharged.

At the movies:

He: Can you see okay?

She: Yes.

He: Is there a draft on you?

She: No.

He: Is your seat comfortable?

She: Yes, fine.

He: Will you change places with me?

Judy: What did one flea say to the other while standing
    on a street corner?
Trudy: I have no idea, what?
Judy: I'm taking a Greyhound to Fifty-sixth Street.

Fran: I had a fall last night which left me unconscious
    for several hours.
Dan: That's a shame! Where did you fall?
Fran: I fell asleep.

Question: What did the red traffic light say to the
    green traffic light?
Answer: I wonder where the yellow went.

Ellen: Did you know that not all the animals that came
    to Noah's ark came in pairs?
Helen: Which ones didn't?
Ellen: The worms came in apples.

Pat: Would you hit a twelve-inch nail with a hammer,
    Matt?
Matt: Not if it were on the foot of the Jolly Green
    Giant!

Fred: I saw something last night I'll never get over!
Ed: What was that?
Fred: The moon.

Little Evie: Don't you like to play with paper dolls
    any more?
Little Ernie: No. I cut them out long ago.

Ted: Do you know why an acrobat's life is like a girl's underwear?

Jed: No, why?

Ted: Because one slip is enough.

Leo: What is green, lies in a ditch, and is covered with cookie crumbs?

Len: A girl scout who has fainted.

Randy: Yes, I have a little balance in the bank, but I got engaged three months ago, and now . . .

Sandy: Ah, love makes the world go round.

Randy: Yes, but I didn't think it would go round so fast that it would make me lose my balance.

Slim: I get up when the first ray of sunshine strikes my window.

Jim: Isn't that kind of early?

Slim: No. My room faces west.

Two eight-year-old boys were looking at an abstract painting in a gift shop. "Let's run," said one, "before they say we did it."

Bob: What candy bar is just for girls?

Rob: Her she (Hershey).

Fred: Why can't a teen-age girl run away from home?

Ted: I give up. Why?

Fred: Because every time she gets to the door, the telephone rings.

Sam: Where did he meet her?

Pam: They met in a revolving door, and he's been going around with her ever since.

Fat Man (in a theater to a little boy sitting behind him): Can you see, sonny?

Boy: Not at all, mister.

Fat Man: Then just watch me and laugh when I do.

Jack: Did you hear the joke about the boy who popped the potato-chip bag?

Mack: No.

Jack: It's crumby.

Harry: What did one ant say to the other while they were floating in a piece of watermelon?

Larry: I don't know. What?

Harry: We're floating in the Rhine.

Solly: What did the moon-boy say to the moon-girl?

Holly: How romantic! There's a beautiful full earth out tonight.

A man who liked to play practical jokes sent his friend a collect telegram that read, "I am feeling fine."

About a week later the joker received a heavy package on which he was required to pay the postage. Opening it, he found a big block of concrete and a note reading: "This is the weight your telegram lifted from my mind."

Question: Where's the best place to hide a lawyer?
Answer: In a legal case.

Leo: Why do you say *amen* in a church instead of *awomen*?
Cleo: I don't know, why?
Leo: Because you sing hymns, not hers.

Question: What is a man called who steals ham?
Answer: A hamburglar.

Meg: Do you have hot water at your house?
Peg: We sure do. And I'm always in it.

Jim: I had a bad dream last night and chewed the
    insides out of the pillow.
Tim: Did you feel sick today?
Jim: No, just a little down in the mouth.

Joe: What has six feet and sings?
Moe: A trio.

Mrs. Dilly and Mrs. Dally met on the street. "Oh,
Sadie," said Mrs. Dilly, "so many things have happened
since I talked to you last. I've had all my teeth removed,
and a new storm door and refrigerator put in."

Did you ever see?????
    A salad bowl?
    A home run?
    A king fish?
    A fire fly?
    A ginger snap?
    A picket fence?
    A square dance?
    A shoe box?
    A hot dog stand?
    A key punch?
    A ball park?

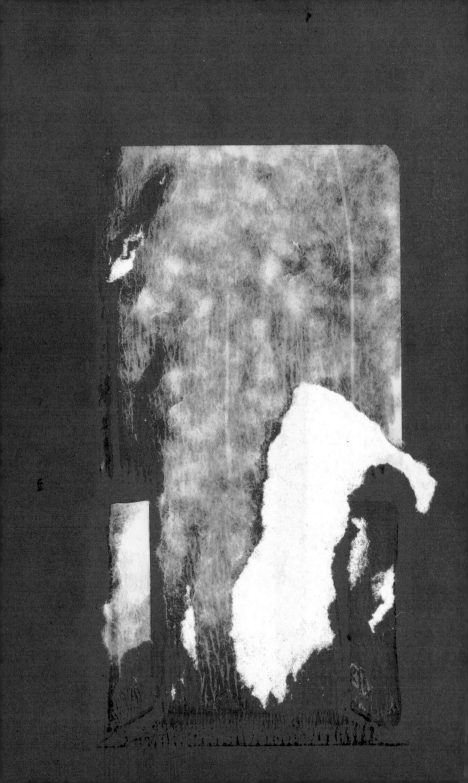